STORY COMPREHENSION To Go ®

Rosemary Huisingh
Linda Bowers
Paul Johnson
Carolyn LoGiudice
Jane Orman

Skill Area:	Reading Comprehension
Ages:	7 through 10
Grades:	2 through 5

LinguiSystems

LinguiSystems, Inc.
3100 4th Avenue
East Moline, IL 61244-9700
1-800 PRO IDEA
1-800-776-4332

FAX: 1-800-577-4555
E-mail: service@linguisystems.com
Web: www.linguisystems.com
TDD: 1-800-933-8331
(for those with hearing impairments)

Printed in the U.S.A.

ISBN 0-7606-0481-9

About the Authors ··························

From the left: Rosemary Huisingh, Jane Orman, Paul Johnson, Carolyn LoGiudice, Linda Bowers

Our lively team of speech-language pathologists and educators includes LinguiSystems owners and employees. We collaborated to develop *Story Comprehension To Go*. Together we have many years of experience in working with students to boost their language, thinking, and reading skills. We share a zest for life and a passion for high-quality instruction for all students. We hope the materials we present reflect our philosophy.

Cover design by Mike Paustian

Illustrations by Margaret Warner

Page layout by Christine Buysse

Table of Contents ·····························

Introduction ··

Story Comprehension To Go was developed for students in grades 2-5, especially those who have difficulty with reading comprehension tasks. It includes numerous brief reading passages with reading comprehension questions for each one. This resource does not address decoding; it highlights essential reading comprehension tasks, including these:

Detecting the main idea
Recalling details
Vocabulary and semantics
Comparing and contrasting
Exclusion
Problem solving
Characters and actions
Figurative language
Predicting
Making inferences
Drawing conclusions
Paraphrasing
Summarizing

The readability of the passages is controlled, based on the Flesch-Kincaid readability statistics. These statistics were revised in 2002; the new statistics yield a higher grade level in most cases than the previous ones. The range in readability is from grade levels 2.0 through 4.9. Each section includes ten passages with the following readability ranges:

Passages 1-4   Readability 2.0-2.9

Passages 5-8   Readability 3.0-3.9

Passages 9-10   Readability 4.0-4.9

The question pages for each passage also ask students to formulate questions about what they have read. The last task for each passage is a related writing prompt.

Use these passages for groups of students or individuals. Photocopy the material so each student has a copy. Encourage your students to highlight or underline key information as they read each passage and to jot down any questions they have.

Research proves that repeated readings improve reading comprehension and that three readings are usually sufficient repetition for a student to grasp the content, assuming a passage is at or below the student's reading competency level. We recommend training students to read a passage three times for adequate comprehension before trying to answer the comprehension questions.

The reading comprehension questions are similar to those found on classroom and national reading comprehension tests. Have your students read each possible answer for the multiple-choice questions before they select their answers.

The answers for most of the comprehension questions are listed in the answer key in the back of this book. In some cases, the answers are just examples of appropriate responses. Accept all logical responses as correct.

As you present this information to your students, model your own reading comprehension strategies. Talk about ways to rescan a passage to find key information and other tips that will help your students improve their reading competence and confidence.

We hope you will find this book a welcome resource to help students understand and find satisfaction in what they read.

Rosemary, Linda, Paul, Carolyn, and Jane

Jack has a job. He works at the toy store. His job is sweeping the floor.
Jack doesn't get paid. He took a toy from the store. He didn't pay for it. Jack
got caught with the toy. He knew it was wrong to take something. Jack told the
store owner he was sorry. Jack knows that stealing doesn't pay. Jack sweeps
the store to show he is sorry. Jack told his mom and dad he won't take anything
again. He told the store owner the same thing. Jack promises to be good.

Vocabulary and Semantics 1, *continued*

Main Idea and Details

1. What is the main idea of this story?
   a. Jack has a job sweeping at a toy store.
   b. Jack works at a toy store.
   c. Jack works because he took a toy.

2. What did Jack do that was wrong?
   a. Took some candy
   b. Took something that didn't belong to him
   c. Took a toy without paying
   d. Both *b* and *c*

3. Who did Jack tell he was sorry and he wouldn't do it again?
   a. The store owner
   b. His mom
   c. The store owner and his mom and dad

Vocabulary and Semantics

4. In the story, Jack took a toy. What does **took** mean in this story?
   a. Chose
   b. Stole
   c. Swiped
   d. Both *b* and *c*

5. What is another word for **buy**?
   a. Take
   b. Purchase
   c. Lose

6. What does **crime doesn't pay** mean?

    a. People often get caught when they steal and have to pay a fine.

    b. People don't get away with taking things.

    c. You can't get much money for stolen things.

    d. Both *a* and *b*

7. Which word means the opposite of **wrong**?

    a. Right

    b. Correct

    c. Incorrect

    d. Both *a* and *b*

Asking Questions

Ask me a question about stealing.

Writing Prompt ·

Pretend you are Jack. Write down what you would say to apologize for taking the toy. Also write your promise not to take things in the future.

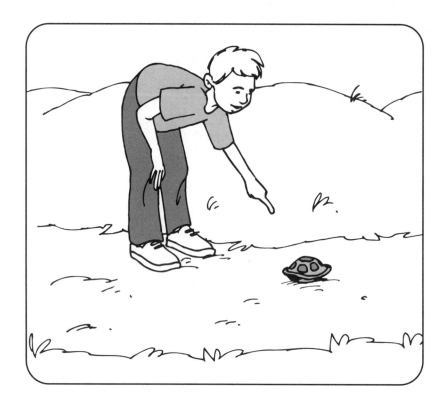

Ray went for a walk. He needed a school project. He saw something on the path. It looked like a rock. The rock moved. Ray looked closer. It was a turtle. He picked it up. The turtle pulled its head into its shell. It pulled in its legs and its tail. Ray put the turtle down. He waited. Out came the turtle's head. The turtle opened its mouth. Ray saw no teeth. The turtle had a beak. The beak looked sharp. Ray touched the turtle. The turtle pulled its head in. Ray got his school project.

Vocabulary and Semantics 2, *continued*

Main Idea and Details

1. What is the main idea of this story?

    a. Ray found a school project.

    b. Ray watched a turtle.

    c. The turtle pulled in its body parts.

2. What did Ray think he saw on the path?

    a. A rock

    b. An animal

    c. A brick

3. What happened when Ray picked up the turtle the first time?

    a. The turtle flipped over.

    b. The story doesn't say.

    c. The turtle pulled in its head, legs, and tail.

Vocabulary and Semantics

4. What is another way to say **school project**?

    a. Special book

    b. Special assignment

    c. Special classwork

    d. Both *b* and *c*

5. What did Ray do after he put the turtle down?

    a. He waited and he watched.

    b. He picked up the turtle again.

    c. He touched the turtle's shell.

6. What did Ray see when the turtle opened its mouth?

    a. No teeth but a beak

    b. No teeth and no beak

    c. No teeth, but a beak and a sharp tongue

7. The turtle had a sharp beak. Which of these things could be sharp?

    a. Knife and spoon

    b. Knife and scissors

    c. Knife and needle

    d. Both *b* and *c*

8. The turtle had a beak. What is a turtle's **beak**?

    a. The part of a turtle's jaw that grabs and cuts food

    b. A turtle's forehead

    c. A turtle's tongue

Asking Questions

Ask me a question about turtles.

Writing Prompt ·

Pretend you are Ray. Make a list of at least six things you saw as you watched the turtle.

Vocabulary and Semantics 3 ··············

Don's ball team is very good. They have won every game this year. They have two more games to play. If they win one game, they are the best team in the city. Everyone thinks they will win the city title.

The Cubs have two outs and Don is up to bat. He swings and connects. It's a fly ball. It goes to center field. As Don rounds second base, the fielder throws to third. Don slides into third. He hears a cracking sound. He feels a knife-like jab in his leg. He grabs his calf. He winces in pain. Don is hurt and he is out. He can't stand up. Everyone is sad because Don's season is over. The Cubs have one more chance to win the city title.

Vocabulary and Semantics 3, *continued*

Main Idea and Details

1. Which is the best title for this story?
   a. Don's Ball Season
   b. The Cubs' Ball Game
   c. The Cubs Win

2. What does everyone think Don's ball team will do?
   a. Tie the game today
   b. Win fewer ball games than any other team
   c. Win the city title

3. How many outs did the Cubs have when Don came to bat?
   a. None
   b. Two
   c. Three

Vocabulary and Semantics

4. Which sentence describes what Don is doing in the sentence **Don is up to bat**?
   a. Don is ready to get a bat.
   b. Don is holding the bat, waiting for the pitch.
   c. Don is waiting in line to bat.

5. In the sentence **Don swings and connects**, what does **connects** mean?
   a. Hits the ball
   b. Misses the ball
   c. Sees the ball fly

6. In the sentence **Don winces in pain**, what is Don doing?

    a. Frowning to show pain

    b. Grabbing his leg to show pain

    c. Curling into a ball to show pain

    d. All of the above

7. What does the word **calf** mean in this story?

    a. A small animal or baby cow

    b. A body part

    c. The lower part of Don's leg

    d. Both *b* and *c*

Asking Questions

Ask me a question about the pain in Don's leg.

Writing Prompt •

Pretend you are on Don's ball team. Write a letter to him to cheer him up. Talk about his season and how your team misses him.

Kim and Devon were riding their bikes. Eric, the neighborhood bully, yelled at them to move. "Out of my way," he said. He rode his bike toward them.

Kim and Devon tried to ignore Eric. He bumped Kim. She landed on the pavement. Her glasses were crumpled and her arm was bleeding. She started to cry.

"Come on, Kim," said Devon. "Let's go to my house. My mom can help us figure out what to do. This street is big enough for all of us to be on," he said. Kim and Devon walked their bikes to Devon's house.

Vocabulary and Semantics 4, *continued*

Main Idea and Details

1. Which is the best title for this story?
   a. A Bad Bike Ride
   b. Kim and Devon Like Their Bikes
   c. Going My Way

2. Who was riding bikes?
   a. Kim, Eric, and Don
   b. Kim, Devon, and Eric
   c. Kim, Devon, and their friend

3. What does the **bully** do in this story?
   a. He bumps into Kim.
   b. He tells Kim and Devon to get out of his way.
   c. He rides bikes with Kim and Devon.
   d. Both *a* and *b*

Vocabulary and Semantics

4. Kim's glasses were crumpled. What does **crumpled** mean?
   a. Bent
   b. Smacked
   c. Crooked
   d. Both *a* and *c*

5. Kim and Devon ignored Eric. What does that mean?
   a. Kim and Devon didn't pay attention to Eric.
   b. Kim and Devon talked to Eric.
   c. Kim and Devon walked away with Eric.

6. Kim landed on the pavement. What is **pavement**?

   a. The street

   b. Cement

   c. A hard surface

   d. All of the above

7. Eric said, "Out of my way." What is another word he could have used?

   a. Move

   b. Go

   c. Stop

8. What is a neighborhood?

   a. A place where people live

   b. A place where people learn

   c. A place where people swim

Asking Questions

Ask me a question about a bully.

Writing Prompt •

Make a list of at least five things Kim and Devon could do to get along with Eric.

Tina has a new friend named Mrs. Hand. Mrs. Hand lives around the corner from Tina in an old, rundown house that needs a lot of work. Tina likes to go there. Tina helps Mrs. Hand bake cookies. They go for walks together at the park. Mrs. Hand knows all about trees and nature. She teaches Tina lots of things.

One day Tina and Mrs. Hand went to the park. Mrs. Hand showed Tina a wolf spider. Mrs. Hand said it lives in the ground in a hole. The hole has a trap door with hinges. Mrs. Hand said when the spider closes the door, nothing can get it, so it is safe. Mrs. Hand is very smart.

Vocabulary and Semantics 5, *continued*

Main Idea and Details

1. Which is the best title for this story?

   a. Tina's New Friend

   b. Mrs. Hand Is Fun

   c. Jennifer Likes Nature

2. What does Tina do with Mrs. Hand?

   a. Bakes cookies and goes for walks in the park

   b. Plays with her

   c. Watches for wolf spiders

3. Where does Mrs. Hand live?

   a. Across the street from Tina

   b. Down the street from Tina

   c. Around the corner from Tina

Vocabulary and Semantics

4. In the story, what does **old, rundown house** mean?

   a. A house that is falling down

   b. An old house that needs lots of work

   c. An old house that needs repair

   d. Both *b* and *c*

5. The spider closes its door. What is a synonym for **closes**?

   a. Blocks

   b. Shuts

   c. Bars

6. The wolf spider is safe in its hole in the ground. What does **safe** mean?

   a. Free from danger

   b. Protected from harm

   c. Away from injury

   d. All of the above

7. Tina likes to visit with Mrs. Hand. Circle all the things **visit** means in the story.

   a. Talk to Mrs. Hand and ask her questions

   b. Go to Mrs. Hand's house

   c. Stay overnight at Mrs. Hand's

   d. Both *a* and *b*

Asking Questions

Ask me a question about friends.

Writing Prompt ••

Pretend you are Tina. Send a thank-you note to Mrs. Hand for helping you write a paper about owls.

Jessie heard a knock at the door and opened it. "Oh, my gosh!" he said. There were seven of his best friends. They were dressed up like pirates. It was Jessie's birthday. His dad had planned a surprise for Jessie. Jessie and his friends were going on a treasure hunt.

Mr. Judd took the pirates to the beach. He explained the rules for the treasure hunt. The boys and girls used maps to find buried treasures. The team that found the most won a prize. Everyone had fun. Jessie was sure this was his best party ever!

Vocabulary and Semantics 6, *continued*

Main Idea and Details

1. Which is the best title for this story?
   a. Jessie Gets Rich
   b. Jessie Has a Birthday
   c. Jessie's Surprise Birthday Party

2. Who planned the party?
   a. Jessie
   b. Jessie's mom
   c. Jessie's dad

3. Who came to the party?
   a. Jessie's family
   b. Jessie's neighbors
   c. Jessie's friends

Vocabulary and Semantics

4. In the sentence **His dad planned a surprise party**, who does **his** refer to?
   a. Jessie
   b. Mr. Judd
   c. Jessie's friend

5. What do we call the special clothing Jessie and his friends wore to the party?
   a. Play clothes
   b. Swimsuits
   c. Costumes

6. In the story when Jessie opened the door, he said, "Oh, my gosh!" What did he mean?

   a. Look out!

   b. I don't believe it!

   c. Where are you?

7. In this story, what is **buried treasure**?

   a. Junk heaped in a pile

   b. Turtle eggs

   c. Things hidden under the sand

8. In this story, the children went on a treasure hunt. What is a **treasure hunt**?

   a. Trying to find things that are hidden

   b. Using a map to find things someone buried

   c. Looking for money in the sand

   d. Both *a* and *b*

Asking Questions

Ask me a question about the map.

Writing Prompt ••

Pretend you are planning a treasure hunt. Make a map and write the rules for the treasure hunt. Make a list of at least five things that you could bury for the treasure hunt.

Mrs. Hill is ill and asked Kyle to dog sit. Kyle needs to feed Winston, walk him, and play with him twice a day. Winston is a happy dog. He likes to run and jump. Kyle uses an old rag and plays tug-of-war with Winston.

This morning Kyle fed Winston and then it was time to play. Kyle forgot to close the gate. Winston spied the open gate and bolted through it. He ran down the street and through Mrs. Hill's flower bed. He ran around her house and into her water fountain. Kyle could not coax Winston out of the water.

Kyle spotted a rug near Mrs. Hill's back door. He grabbed it and waved it toward Winston. Winston leaped from the water and quickly joined the tug-of-war game.

Vocabulary and Semantics 7, *continued*

Main Idea and Details

1. What is the main idea of this story?
    a. Kyle's dog-sitting experience
    b. Mrs. Stone is ill.
    c. Kyle and Winston play tug-of-war.

2. What jobs must Kyle do when he dog sits?
    a. Feed, walk, and play with Winston
    b. Keep Winston in the yard
    c. Play tug-of-war with Winston

3. When Kyle spotted a rug near Mrs. Hill's back door, what did he do?
    a. Left it there
    b. Picked it up
    c. Grabbed it and waved it

Vocabulary and Semantics

4. What does it mean to **dog sit**?
    a. Play with the dog
    b. Walk the dog
    c. Take care of the dog

5. What does **spied the open gate** mean in the story?
    a. Walked through the open gate
    b. Saw the open gate
    c. Noticed the open gate
    d. Both *b* and *c*

Vocabulary and Semantics 7, *continued*

6. What does **coax** mean in **Kyle could not coax Winston out of the water**?

   a. Pull him out

   b. Make him come out

   c. Persuade him to come out

   d. Both *b* and *c*

7. What does **bolted through the gate** mean in the story?

   a. Looked through the open gate

   b. Walked over to the open gate

   c. Ran quickly through the open gate

Asking Questions

Ask me a question about this story.

Writing Prompt ••

Imagine you are Kyle. Write the story you will tell Mrs. Hill about your dog-sitting experience.

The Woods family is ready for vacation. Last night they loaded the van with food, clothes, and camping gear. Early this morning, they headed to State Park. The whole family was excited. Tom wanted to swim and hike. Jim wanted to fish and boat.

When they got to camp, everyone hurried to pitch the tent. They unpacked the van and went inside the tent. Suddenly there was a loud rumble, a sharp clap, and a bang. Oh, no! The fun would have to wait!

Vocabulary and Semantics 8, *continued*

Main Idea and Details

1. What is the main idea of this story?
    a. The Woods family's vacation
    b. The Woods family is excited about swimming.
    c. The Woods family stayed in a tent.

2. Where did the Woods family go for vacation?
    a. To a tent
    b. To a lake
    c. To State Park

3. What did the Woods family want to do on vacation?
    a. Go swimming, hiking, fishing, and boating
    b. Go hiking, biking, and fishing
    c. Go swimming, biking, and hiking

Vocabulary and Semantics

4. What does **packed the van** mean in this story?
    a. Put toys and food in the van
    b. Put food, clothes, and camping gear in the van
    c. Put everything for vacation in the van
    d. All of the above

5. What does **pitch the tent** mean in this story?
    a. Get the tent out
    b. Put the tent up
    c. Take the tent down

6. There was a loud rumble, a sharp clap, and a bang. What was happening in the story?

   a. A storm was coming.

   b. Someone was making noise.

   c. Something was outside the tent.

7. In this story, the whole family was excited about their vacation. What's another word we could use for **excited**?

   a. Eager

   b. Upset

   c. Unhappy

8. The Woods family loaded the van and headed to State Park. What does **headed to** mean in the story?

   a. Drove to State Park

   b. Got to State Park

   c. Found State Park

Asking Questions

Ask me a question about the story.

Writing Prompt •••

Pretend you are a member of the Woods family. Write about the storm. Write three fun things you could do during the storm.

The grade school show was ready to begin. The audience was waiting quietly. "I can't go on. I'm too nervous," Maria said. "Sure you can. You know your lines," said Joe. Their teacher grinned and whispered, "Break a leg, everyone!"

The curtain opened and Joe, Maria, and Ned were standing in front of the crowd. They sang and danced. They said their lines perfectly. The crowd clapped loudly. The performers smiled and smiled.

Mrs. Jones was waiting backstage to congratulate her happy students. The show was wonderful.

Vocabulary and Semantics 9, *continued*

Main Idea and Details

1. What is the main idea of this story?

   a. A grade school show

   b. Maria and Joe are friends.

   c. The audience waits.

2. What was the audience doing before the show started?

   a. Waiting for the show to start

   b. Singing

   c. Talking

3. Who was nervous?

   a. Joe

   b. Maria

   c. Ned

Vocabulary and Semantics

4. What is an audience?

   a. The children, or performers, in the program

   b. The people watching the show

   c. The teacher

5. Mrs. Jones whispered, "Break a leg, everyone!" What does that mean in the story?

   a. She wants everyone to fall and break a leg.

   b. She wants everyone to get out on stage.

   c. It's a good luck wish for everyone.

6. Mrs. Jones congratulated the performers. What do you think she said?

   a. "I know you can do better next time."

   b. "We need more practice to do better."

   c. "Great job, everyone!"

7. What does **performer** mean in the story?

   a. The people watching the show

   b. The teacher

   c. The children who sang, talked, and danced in the show

Asking Questions

Ask me a question about the performers.

Writing Prompt ••

Look at the picture. Pretend you are one of the performers. Write the song you would sing in the show. Then write what you would say in the show.

Every summer Ann and her mother have a special day together. Today they went to a park. They rode the Ferris wheel and some water rides. They were so busy, they got very hungry. They bought popcorn and a hot dog. When they sat down to eat, the hot dog had disappeared.

Main Idea and Details

1. What is the main idea of this story?

   a. Every summer Ann and her mother go shopping.

   b. Every summer Ann and her mother have a special day together.

   c. Every summer Ann and her mother go to the park.

2. Where did Ann and her mother go?

   a. To a pool

   b. To get a hot dog

   c. To a park

3. What did Ann and her mother do at the park?

   a. They rode the Ferris wheel and went home.

   b. They rode the Ferris wheel and some other rides.

   c. They went on rides and ate.

Vocabulary and Semantics

4. What is an amusement park?

   a. A place that has rides and games

   b. A place to have fun

   c. A place to eat

   d. All of the above

5. What does **disappeared** mean in the story?

   a. Fell apart

   b. Was gone

   c. Was cold

6. Ann and her mother had a special day. What does **special day** mean in the story?

    a. Not like every day

    b. Like every day

    c. Different from every day

    d. Both *a* and *c*

7. What are **water rides**?

    a. Rides that go underwater (like a submarine)

    b. Rides that go on water (like a canoe or boat)

    c. Rides that go through water (like a log splash or waterfall)

    d. All of the above

Asking Questions

Ask me a question about amusement parks.

Writing Prompt •

Explain what you think happened to the hot dog.

Sequencing 1

Kara sighs as the bus stops in front of her. She slowly climbs up the steps. She doesn't know why her mom had to get a new job, and now she has to go to this new school. She starts down the aisle of the bus, looking at her feet and frowning. Just then someone begins saying her name, and she looks up.

"Kara, is that you? Is your name Kara? Sit here with me." Kara looks at the girl who is smiling at her. She remembers her mom telling her about a girl she might meet.

"Thanks," says Kara, smiling a little. She sits down and says, "Are you Beth? Your mom works with my mom, right?"

"Yes, I am. I was hoping we would ride the same bus," says Beth. "My mom said I should look for you. How do you feel about changing schools?"

"I'm a little scared," says Kara. "I don't know anyone at this school."

"Now you know me," Beth says. "I think we're going to become good friends. Do you want to come over after school?"

"Sure," says Kara. "I'll have to ask my mom first."

"I have a new CD we can listen to," Beth says.

"That sounds like fun," says Kara. She was starting to feel a little less scared about this new school.

Sequencing 1, *continued*

Main Idea and Details

1. Which title would be better for this story?

    a. Kara Makes a New Friend

    b. First Day at a New School

2. How do Kara's and Beth's moms know each other?

    a. They go to college together.

    b. They work together.

    c. They are in the same club.

3. What are Kara and Beth going to do at Beth's place after school?

    a. Play games

    b. Do homework

    c. Listen to a CD

Sequencing

4. What part of the story does the picture show?

    a. Beginning

    b. Middle

    c. End

5. What happens at the beginning of the story?

    a. Kara walks down the bus aisle.

    b. Kara gets on the bus.

    c. Beth calls Kara's name.

6. Which of these things happens last?

   a. Beth calls Kara's name.

   b. Kara gets on the bus.

   c. Kara sits with Beth.

7. What does Kara have to do before she can go to Beth's house?

   a. Finish her homework

   b. Ask her mom

   c. Do her chores

8. Does this story take place before or after school? Explain how you can tell.

Asking Questions

Ask me a question about making a new friend.

Writing Prompt ••

Make a list of things that make someone a good friend.

Sequencing 2 ···

Chad hates washing dishes. He sits at the table and frowns. It is covered with dirty dishes. He knows he has to do it. It is almost time for *Star Cruiser*. That is his favorite show. He has to do the dishes first. Then he can watch the show.

He clears the table. He stacks the dishes in the sink. Chad runs warm water. He adds some soap as the water runs. He washes the dishes. Then he dries them. He puts them away.

Chad is almost done. He wipes off the table. He wipes off the counter. Then he turns off the light. Now he can watch his show. When it is over, he will go to bed.

Sequencing 2, *continued*

Main Idea and Details

1. Which title would be better for this story?
   a. Chad Watches His Favorite Show
   b. Chad's Least Favorite Chore

2. How does Chad feel about doing the dishes?
   a. He likes it.
   b. He hates it.
   c. He needs help.

3. What is *Star Cruiser*?
   a. A TV show
   b. A book
   c. A vehicle

Sequencing

4. What part of the story does the picture show?
   a. Beginning
   b. Middle
   c. End

5. What does Chad get to do after he finishes the dishes?
   a. Watch *Star Cruiser*
   b. Go to bed
   c. Do his homework

6. When did Chad add soap to the water?

    a. After he filled the sink with water

    b. As he was filling the sink with water

    c. Before he started filling the sink with water

7. What is the last thing Chad does before leaving the kitchen?

    a. Turns off the lights

    b. Wipes off the counter

    c. Puts the dishes away

8. At what time of day does this story take place? Explain how you can tell.

Asking Questions

Ask me a question about washing dishes.

Writing Prompt ••

What is your least favorite chore? Why?

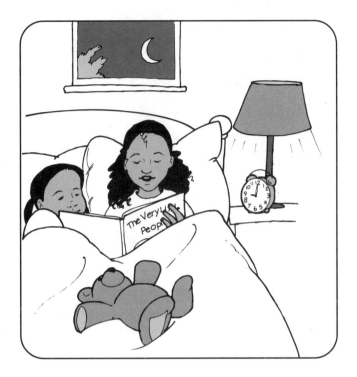

Jackie can't fall asleep. She went to bed about an hour ago. She is still awake. She can hear her big sister in the room next door.

Jackie grabs a book. Then she grabs her teddy bear. She walks into her sister's room. "Vicky, will you read to me?" Jackie asks. "I can't get to sleep."

"Come in here," Vicky says. Jackie climbs into the bed. Vicky starts to read. She reads the first page. Then she looks at Jackie. She is fast asleep.

Sequencing 3, *continued*

Main Idea and Details

1. Which title would be better for this story?

   a. Jackie Finally Goes to Sleep

   b. Vicky Reads a Bedtime Story

2. What two things does Jackie take to Vicky's room?

   a. A teddy bear and a doll

   b. A doll and a book

   c. A teddy bear and a book

3. Where is Jackie's sister's room?

   a. Across the hall

   b. Next door

   c. Downstairs

Sequencing

4. What part of the story does the picture show?

   a. Beginning

   b. Middle

   c. End

5. What happened first after Jackie went into Vicky's room?

   a. Jackie fell asleep.

   b. Jackie got into bed with Vicky.

   c. Vicky took Jackie back to her room.

Sequencing 3, *continued*

6. What did Jackie do before she left her own bedroom?

    a. Grabbed her teddy bear and a book

    b. Turned off the lights

    c. Talked to Vicky

7. What did Vicky do after Jackie got into bed with her?

    a. Told Jackie to come into her room

    b. Took Jackie back to her own room

    c. Read Jackie a story

8. What do you think Vicky will do with Jackie next? Explain your answer.

Asking Questions

Ask me a question about going to bed.

> **Writing Prompt** ••
>
> What do you do when you can't go to sleep at night?

Mario and Beth went hiking. They hiked all morning. The first thing they saw was a baby deer. Then they saw the deer's mother. Next they saw a squirrel. It ran up a tree. They enjoyed the fresh air. Hiking in the woods was fun.

They stopped hiking at noon. It was lunch time. They opened their backpacks. They ate their sandwiches. They drank some water. They talked about the things they had seen.

Main Idea and Details

1. Which title would be better for this story?
    a. An Excellent Morning of Hiking
    b. Mario and Beth Eat Lunch Together

2. Where were Mario and Beth hiking?
    a. The desert
    b. The mountains
    c. The woods

3. At what time did Mario and Beth eat lunch?
    a. Noon
    b. Eleven o'clock
    c. Twelve-thirty

Sequencing

4. What part of the story does the picture show?
    a. Beginning
    b. Middle
    c. End

5. What was the first thing Mario and Beth saw on their hike?
    a. A stream
    b. A baby deer
    c. A squirrel

6. What did Mario and Beth do first after they decided to have lunch?

   a. Drank water

   b. Ate sandwiches

   c. Opened their backpacks

7. What did Mario and Beth do while they were eating lunch?

   a. Talked about what they saw

   b. Watched the wildlife

   c. Looked at a stream

8. What do you think Mario and Beth will do after they eat their lunch? Explain your answer.

Asking Questions

Ask me a question about hiking.

Writing Prompt ••

What would you expect to see if you went on a hike in the forest?

"How about strawberry? No, I'll have chocolate chip. Oh, I can't decide," says Tanya.

"Honey, we have to pick up Mom in a few minutes. You need to make up your mind," Dad says.

"But there are so many flavors to choose from. I don't know how I can pick just one," says Tanya.

"I'm afraid you will have to, Tanya," says Dad. "I told you if you helped me clean the house, I'd buy you an ice cream cone. I can't pick the flavor for you, though. You have about thirty seconds to make up your mind or we will be late picking up your mom."

"Hey, I have an idea," Tanya says, smiling. Then she says to the person behind the counter, "One scoop of strawberry and one scoop of chocolate chip in a cone, please."

Tanya's dad looks at her and smiles. "Now, that's a great way to solve a problem," he says. Then they got in the car to go pick up Tanya's mom.

Sequencing 5, *continued*

Main Idea and Details

1. Which title would be better for this story?
    a. Tanya Helps Her Dad
    b. Tanya Solves a Problem

2. Where does this story take place?
    a. At home
    b. At a car wash
    c. In an ice cream store

3. How many scoops of ice cream does Tanya get?
    a. One
    b. Two
    c. Three

Sequencing

4. What part of the story does the picture show?
    a. Beginning
    b. Middle
    c. End

5. What were Tanya and her dad doing before they went to the ice cream store?
    a. Going for a walk
    b. Picking up Tanya's mom
    c. Cleaning the house

6. What are Tanya and her dad going to do after they leave the ice cream store?

   a. Pick up Tanya's mom

   b. Go home

   c. Wash the car

7. Which thing happened first in the story?

   a. Tanya and her dad went to pick up Tanya's mom.

   b. Tanya's dad told her she had thirty seconds to decide.

   c. Tanya decided to get one scoop of strawberry and one scoop of chocolate chip.

8. Do you agree with this statement? **Tanya knew what kind of ice cream she would get before she got to the store.** Explain your answer.

Asking Questions

Ask me a question about ice cream.

Writing Prompt •

Invent a new flavor of ice cream. What ingredients are in it? What steps do you take to make it?

Max and his dad spend most Saturdays together. Last Saturday they weren't able to be together because Max's dad had to work. Max is really looking forward to this Saturday.

His dad picks him up at eight o'clock in the morning. They go out for a big breakfast at Pancake Village. Then his dad says, "I think we'll go see Grandpa this morning. He is thinking about selling his old car. I thought we'd wash it up for him."

"I guess the car might sell better if it's clean," Max said.

"I think you're right," said Max's dad.

Max and his dad worked for two hours on Grandpa's car. They washed and dried it. Then they waxed it. The last thing they did was clean the inside. Grandpa came out to look at the car when they were done. He thought the car looked great.

Max had a great time helping his dad. He couldn't think of a better way to spend a Saturday.

Main Idea and Details

1. Which title would be better for this story?

    a. Max and His Dad Have a Great Saturday

    b. Max and His Dad Wax the Car

2. What two places did Max and his dad go?

    a. Pancake Village, car wash

    b. Pancake Village, Grandpa's house

    c. Car wash, Grandpa's house

3. On what day of the week does this story take place?

    a. Saturday

    b. Sunday

    c. Friday

Sequencing

4. What is the first place that Max and his dad went?

    a. Pancake Village

    b. Grandpa's house

    c. Grocery store

5. What did Max and his dad do after they got to Grandpa's house?

    a. Ate lunch

    b. Washed the car

    c. Had pancakes

Readability 3.2
Story Comprehension To Go   53

6. What is Grandpa going to do with the car after it is clean?

   a. Sell it

   b. Give it to someone

   c. Leave it in the garage

7. Why didn't Max and his dad spend last Saturday together?

   a. His dad was visiting Grandpa.

   b. His dad forgot to pick him up.

   c. His dad had to work.

8. Why did Max and his dad wash the car before Grandpa was going to sell it?

Asking Questions

Ask me a question about washing the car.

Writing Prompt •

What is your favorite day of the week? Explain why that is your favorite day.

Jay has a geography test today. He studied for two hours last night. He has South America down cold. He is confident about doing well. Jay is not nervous when Mr. Williams passes out the tests.

The first three questions are easy. Jay writes down the answers. He thinks, "This is going to be an easy *A*." Then he reads the next question. It says, "What are the main exports of Brazil and Chile?" His mind goes blank. He can't remember studying about exports. He starts to get a little nervous. Then he says to himself, "Jay, just relax. Do the rest of the questions and come back to it." That's what he does. By the time he comes back to the question, he remembers what he needs to know.

Jay finishes the test and takes it to Mr. Williams' desk. Mr. Williams looks up and asks, "How was it?" Jay smiles and gives him a thumbs up.

Sequencing 7, *continued*

Main Idea and Details

1. Which title would be better for this story?

   a. Jay Knows a Lot About South America

   b. Jay Makes It Through the Geography Test

2. How many hours did Jay study?

   a. Two

   b. Three

   c. Four

3. What hand sign did Jay give Mr. Williams?

   a. A peace sign

   b. A wave

   c. A thumbs up

Sequencing

4. What part of the story does the picture show?

   a. Beginning

   b. Middle

   c. End

5. What does Jay do after he gets stuck on a question?

   a. Asks Mr. Williams for help

   b. Answers the rest of the questions first

   c. Rereads the first three questions

6. How does Jay feel after he reads the fourth question?

   a. Nervous

   b. Excited

   c. Confident

7. How did Jay feel before the test?

   a. Nervous

   b. Excited

   c. Confident

8. Do you agree with this statement? **Jay doesn't think he did very well on the test.**
   Explain your answer.

Asking Questions

Ask me a question about taking a test.

Writing Prompt •

   What are five things you should do to get ready for a test?

"Is that our boat?" Brittany asks.

"No, we're just renting it for the week," Dad answers. "Are we ready for a ride? Let's take a quick spin around the lake. We will make lunch when we get back."

Dad helps Ryan and Brittany put on their life jackets. He tells them they probably won't need to use the life jackets, but they have to wear them whenever they are in the boat. He says, "If anything happens and you fall in the water, don't panic. Just relax. Your life jacket will keep your head above the water."

Everyone gets into the boat and they take off. They have a fun ride around the lake. Brittany and Ryan like it when Dad makes the boat go really fast and the front sticks out of the water.

Main Idea and Details

1. Which title would be better for this story?
   a. Life Jackets Keep Your Head Above Water
   b. Brittany, Ryan, and Dad Take a Boat Ride

2. For how long is Dad renting the boat?
   a. A day
   b. A week
   c. A month

3. When the boat goes fast, what happens to the front?
   a. It sticks up out of the water.
   b. It dips into the water.
   c. Nothing happens.

Sequencing

4. What part of the story does the picture show?
   a. Beginning
   b. Middle
   c. End

5. What did Dad do before getting in the boat?
   a. Helped Brittany and Ryan put their life jackets on
   b. Made lunch
   c. Made the boat go really fast

Readability 3.9

Story Comprehension To Go

6. What did Dad tell Brittany and Ryan to do if they fall in the water?

   a. Panic

   b. Yell

   c. Relax

7. How does a life jacket help you after you fall into the water?

   a. It keeps you near the boat.

   b. It keeps your head above water.

   c. It keeps you from panicking.

8. During what part of the day does this story take place? Explain how you can tell.

Asking Questions

Ask me a question about riding in a boat.

Writing Prompt •••

Pretend you are going to design your own boat. Draw a picture of it and tell all the things that are special about it.

Marla is home alone. Her parents have gone shopping. They know Marla is a responsible person and can be left alone. Marla's parents have been gone for about an hour. Marla has been working on the computer and watching TV. She decides to go into the kitchen and get a snack.

She opens the kitchen door and notices a strange smell. Just then the smoke alarm goes off. Marla sees smoke around the door to the garage, and she runs back to the living room. She picks up the phone, calls 9-1-1 to report the fire, and runs out the front door. She goes across the street to Mrs. Livingston's house. She stands with Mrs. Livingston on the front lawn and waits for the fire trucks to arrive.

The fire department gets to the house just as Marla's parents are pulling up. Flames and smoke are pouring from the garage. Marla yells at her mom as she gets out of the car. Marla runs over and gives her mom and dad a big hug. "Marla, I'm so glad you are all right," her mom says. "It looks like you knew what to do to stay safe."

Sequencing 9^{, continued}

Main Idea and Details

1. What is the main idea of this story?

   a. Marla stays home alone.

   b. Marla handles an emergency.

2. Where was the phone Marla used to call 9-1-1?

   a. In the kitchen

   b. In the living room

   c. In the bathroom

3. In what part of the house was the fire located?

   a. In the garage

   b. In the kitchen

   c. In the basement

Sequencing

4. What part of the story does the picture show?

   a. Beginning

   b. Middle

   c. End

5. What did Marla do immediately after she smelled smoke and heard the alarm?

   a. Called 911

   b. Went to Mrs. Livingston's house

   c. Ran into the living room

6. What is the last thing Marla did in the story?

   a. Waited on Mrs. Livingston's lawn

   b. Gave her mom and dad a hug

   c. Watched the fire and smoke from the garage

7. What was Marla doing before she went into the kitchen?

   a. Homework

   b. Working on the computer

   c. Listening to the radio

8. Do you agree with this statement? **Marla is a responsible person.** Explain your answer.

Asking Questions

Ask me a question about fire safety.

Writing Prompt ••

Pretend there is a fire in the place where you live. What three things, in order, would you do?

Karen is enjoying a beautiful summer day. She is sitting in her favorite chair with a cold drink. She is watching her kids play with the garden hose. They are yelling and spraying each other and their dog, Scraps. Karen smiles as she watches them play.

Karen sips her drink as Scraps dashes over to her chair. She smiles and says, "Hi, Scraps, old buddy. You sure look wet!" Scraps barks once and immediately begins to shake himself dry. The water he shakes off flies through the air and all over Karen.

Springing to her feet, Karen drops her drink as Scraps runs off. Karen stands there, soaking wet and thinking about how her perfect day has suddenly gone bad. She looks down at her wet clothes and starts to laugh. Since she's soaked already, she decides to join the kids playing with the garden hose.

Main Idea and Details

1. Which title would be better for this story?

    a. Scraps Interrupts Karen's Perfect Day

    b. Karen Enjoys a Perfect Day

2. What does Karen have in her hand at the beginning of the story?

    a. A soda

    b. A cold drink

    c. A cup of coffee

3. What are Karen's kids playing with?

    a. A garden hose

    b. Water balloons

    c. A sprinkler

Sequencing

4. What part of the story does the picture show?

    a. Beginning

    b. Middle

    c. End

5. Match the word that describes how Karen feels in each part of the story.

    a. Beginning   1. Surprised

    b. Middle   2. Content

    c. End   3. Playful

6. What does Karen do as Scraps is shaking water on her?

   a. Springs to her feet

   b. Laughs at Scraps

   c. Falls off her chair

7. What happened first in the story?

   a. Karen sprang from her chair.

   b. Karen played with the garden hose.

   c. The kids sprayed Scraps with water.

8. What was Karen doing to enjoy her day at the beginning of the story? What was she doing to enjoy her day at the end of the story?

Asking Questions

Ask me a question about Scraps.

Writing Prompt •

What is your favorite way to enjoy a warm, sunny day? What is something you would not want to do on a nice day? Explain your answers.

Ashley and Kristin love cats. Ashley found a fluffy, striped tiger cat. Kristin found a sleek, black cat. It had a white patch on its forehead and white socks. Both cats were friendly. The girls picked up the cats. The cats purred.

The girls played with the black cat. They played with the tiger cat. They had fun with them. They did not know how to choose. They asked their father if they could take both cats home.

Dad shook his head and said, "You can have only one cat. It costs too much to feed and care for two animals."

The girls thought about how they could earn some money and asked, "If we do more jobs at home, can we have both cats?"

Dad picked up the tiger cat. It purred. Then he picked up the black cat. It licked his hand. Dad said, "I cannot choose, either. If you promise to do more jobs, you may take both cats."

Comparing and Contrasting 1 , continued

Main Idea and Details

1. What is the main idea of this story?

    a. Ashley and Kristin love cats.

    b. Ashley and Kristin get cats.

2. What did the girls do with the cats?

    a. The girls played with the cats.

    b. The girls took the cats for a walk.

3. What did the girls' dad want them to do?

    a. He wanted them to take one cat home.

    b. He wanted them to buy a dog.

4. What did the girls promise to do so they could have both cats?

    a. They promised the cats would not cost too much money.

    b. They promised to do jobs at home to earn more money.

5. What did Dad do with the cats?

    a. Dad held each cat.

    b. Dad fed each cat.

6. What did the black cat do to Dad?

    a. The black cat purred when Dad held it.

    b. The black cat licked Dad's hand.

Comparing and Contrasting

7. Which sentence tells how the animals are the same?

    a. The animals are cats and they are friendly.

    b. The animals are cats and they are the same color.

Comparing and Contrasting 1, *continued*

8. Which sentence tells one way the animals are different?

   a. One cat is big and the other cat is small.

   b. One cat is black and the other cat is orange with black stripes.

9. Which sentence tells how the markings on the cats are different?

   a. One cat purrs and the other cat licks.

   b. One cat has a white patch on its forehead and white socks. The other cat has tiger stripes.

10. Which sentence tells how Ashley and Kristin felt about cats?

    a. Both girls loved cats.

    b. One girl loved cats more than the other.

Asking Questions

Ask me a question to find out how the cats in this story are different.

Writing Prompt ••

Write about the kind of pet you would like to have. Think about which kind of animal, its color, size, where it will sleep, and how you would take care of it.

Comparing and Contrasting 2 ············

Ted came into the house. He plopped on the couch. His legs were sore and his back ached. He played in a soccer tournament all day.

"Do not sit on the couch, Ted," said his mom. "You are covered with mud. You have to look different to sit on the couch."

Ted knew what his mom meant. The living room couch was new. She wanted to keep mud off it. He had to clean up if he wanted to sit on it. He had mud everywhere. It covered his legs and arms. His hair had mud in it, too. His shirt and pants were dirty. Ted was sleepy. He did not want to take a bath. He wanted to sleep on the couch.

Ted took a bath and scrubbed the mud out of his hair. He put on clean clothes. He brushed his teeth. He told his mom he would come downstairs. He wanted to watch a movie. He went to his bedroom to get a sweatshirt. He sat on the edge of his bed, leaned over, and put his head on the pillow. He fell asleep. His mom found him and decided the movie could wait. Ted could watch it tomorrow. She put a blanket over him. She kissed him good night.

Comparing and Contrasting 2, *continued*

Main Idea and Details

1. What is the main idea of this story?
    a. Ted cleans up and falls asleep.
    b. Ted gets the new couch dirty.
    c. Ted plays a soccer game.

2. Why did Ted have to clean up before he could sit on the couch?
    a. The couch was new and his mom did not want mud on it.
    b. Mud is hard to clean off a couch.
    c. Both *a* and *b*

3. Why didn't Ted watch the movie?
    a. He was so tired, he fell asleep as soon as he lay down.
    b. He decided the movie could wait until tomorrow.
    c. He was upset with his mom for making him clean up.

Comparing and Contrasting

4. Which sentence describes how Ted looked before he took a bath?
    a. He had mud everywhere.
    b. His legs were sore and his back ached.
    c. He knew what his mom meant.

5. Which sentence describes how Ted looked after his bath?
    a. The mud was off his arms, legs, and hair.
    b. Ted put on clean clothes.
    c. Ted could sit on the couch.

6. Which sentence describes how Ted felt before and after his bath?

   a. Ted felt good and decided to watch a movie.

   b. Ted's legs were sore.

   c. Ted felt good and sleepy.

7. Which sentence does not tell how Ted looked before and after his bath?

   a. Ted was covered with mud and washed it off so he could watch a movie.

   b. Ted was tired but happy about the soccer game.

   c. Ted was filthy, but he got the mud off his arm, legs, and hair when he took a bath.

8. Which sentence describes how Ted probably looked before his soccer game?

   a. Ted was clean and wore clean clothes.

   b. Ted had old clothes on because he knew he would get dirty playing soccer.

   c. Both *a* and *b*

Asking Questions

Ask me a question to compare how Ted looked before and after his bath.

Writing Prompt ··

Compare taking a shower to taking a bath to clean off mud.

There are four seasons. Each season has different weather.

Winter weather is cold. Some places have rain. Some places have snow. You can ski or ride a sled in the snow.

Spring comes after winter. The air gets warmer and it rains. The trees and flowers need rain to grow. It is fun to walk in the rain with your umbrella.

Summer comes after spring. It gets hot in the summer. It is a good time to swim and ride your bike outside. It is fun to eat outside, too. You do not need a coat and hat in the summer. You do need sunscreen.

Fall comes after summer. The air gets cooler and the leaves fall off the trees. You will need a sweater or jacket in the fall. It is fun to ride your bike in the fall. Some kids start school in the fall. Another word for **fall** is **autumn**.

Comparing and Contrasting 3, *continued*

Main Idea and Details

1. What is the main idea of this story?

    a. Each season has different weather.

    b. Each season has similar weather patterns.

2. What is summer like?

    a. It is hot in the summer.

    b. You need to wear sunscreen.

    c. You can swim outside in the summer.

    d. All of the above

3. What is fall like?

    a. Leaves fall off the trees in the fall.

    b. It gets cooler in the fall.

    c. The air gets warmer in the fall.

    d. Both *a* and *b*

Comparing and Contrasting

4. Which sentence tells how summer and winter are different?

    a. Summer has nice weather for going outside.

    b. Summer is warmer than winter.

    c. There are fun things to do in the summer and winter.

5. How are fall and spring the same?

    a. Leaves come out in spring and fall off in autumn.

    b. It rains more often in the spring than in the fall.

    c. Both seasons have mild weather.

6. Which sentence tells how summer and spring are the same?

   a. Summer is warmer than spring.

   b. Both seasons are warm.

   c. You might need a sweater or jacket in the spring.

7. How are fall and winter the same?

   a. Days are shorter in the winter.

   b. Some trees lose their leaves in the fall.

   c. Both seasons have cool or cold weather.

8. What can you do outside in the summer that you do inside in the winter?

   a. You have a picnic outside in the summer and inside in the winter.

   b. You swim outside in the summer and inside in the winter.

   c. Both *a* and *b*

Asking Questions

Ask a question to learn how summer and winter are different.

Writing Prompt •

Write a weather report that describes summer and winter in your town.

Kim and Kate are best friends. They talk on the phone. They go to the mall. They do homework together. Most of all they like to ice skate. The girls are different, too. Kim's hair is red. Kate's hair is brown. Kim is the youngest child. Kate is the oldest in her family. Kim shares a room with her sister. Kate has her own room. The girls are in the same grade but are in different classes.

A new girl came to Kim's class. Kim showed Mia around the school. The girls learned they were alike. They liked to talk on the phone. They liked to skate. Kim asked Mia to skate and meet Kate. Mia skated with Kim. Mia raced Kim. Kate asked Mia to race, but Mia had to tie her skate. Kim did not see that Kate was sad.

Kate went home. She did not call Kim. The next day, Kim asked Kate what was wrong. Kate told her about skating with Mia. Kim was sorry. The girls decided to ask Mia and other girls to skate. They had a wonderful time. Having many friends is fun with your best friend.

Comparing and Contrasting 4, *continued*

Main Idea and Details

1. What is the main idea of this story?

   a. Kate goes home without Kim.

   b. Kim gets a new friend.

   c. Kim and Kate are best friends.

2. How do you know that Kim and Kate are best friends?

   a. Kate and Kim are busy at school.

   b. Kate and Kim like to do many things together.

   c. Kate and Kim have homework.

3. Who is the new girl in the story?

   a. Mia

   b. Kim

4. What did Kim ask Mia?

   a. Kim asked Mia to call her.

   b. Kim asked Mia to eat lunch with Kate.

   c. Kim asked Mia to skate and meet Kate.

5. What happened between Mia and Kate?

   a. Mia did not skate with Kate.

   b. Mia skated with Kim.

   c. Mia and Kate skated.

6. How did Kate feel at the skating rink?

   a. Kate was angry.

   b. Kate went home.

   c. Kate was sad.

7. What did Kim say to Kate?

    a. Kim told Kate she was sorry.

    b. Kim told Kate she wanted to skate with Mia.

    c. Kim said, "Let's be friends."

8. What did Kate and Kim do about Mia?

    a. They did not ask Mia to skate.

    b. They asked Mia and other friends to skate.

    c. They skated together.

Comparing and Contrasting

9. Tell the ways Kim and Kate are the same.

    a. They like to talk on the phone, go to the mall, study, and ice skate.

    b. They are in the same class and live on the same street.

    c. They are in the same school but not in the same class.

10. How are Kim and Kate different?

    a. Kim's hair is red and Kate's is brown.

    b. Kim shares a bedroom, but Kate has her own room.

    c. Kim is the youngest in her family, Kate is the oldest.

    d. All of the above

11. Which sentence tells how Kate and Kim are the same?

    a. Kim and Kate like to do many things together.

    b. Kim and Kate are like sisters.

    c. Kim and Kate are in the same class.

12. Which sentence tells how Kim and Kate are different?

    a. Kim and Kate look different and are not in the same class.

    b. Kim and Kate have different friends.

    c. Kim and Kate are in different grades and at different schools.

Asking Questions

Ask me a question to find out how Kim and Kate are the same.

Writing Prompt ···

Write two lists. In the first list, tell how you and a friend are the same. In the second list, tell how you are different.

Sam and Dave are brothers. They were each adopted at age one. Dave came to his family on November 1, 1993. Sam came on November 1, 1996. They live in the house where their dad grew up.

Dave is taller than Sam is. His eyes and hair are brown. He plays football and is on the track team. He plays the piano. He started a business. He mows lawns in the summer. In the winter, he shovels snow. Sam likes to help him.

Sam has blond hair. His eyes are green. He plays basketball and cooks. He likes anything about space. One time he made a rocket. He and Dave launched it in the backyard.

Sam likes to tease Dave. Sam switched jackets with Dave. He told Dave, "Your jacket shrank in the wash. Mine stretched in the wash."

Dave likes to pretend with Sam. Dave tells Sam, "You are funny."

Comparing and Contrasting 5, *continued*

Main Idea and Details

1. What is the main idea of this story?
   a. Sam and Dave were babies together.
   b. Sam and Dave were adopted on the same day.
   c. Describing two brothers, Sam and Dave

2. Where do the boys live?
   a. They live in the house where their dad grew up.
   b. They tease each other at home.
   c. They launch rockets in the backyard.

3. When was Sam adopted?
   a. He was adopted on November 1, 1996.
   b. He was adopted when he was one year old.
   c. He was adopted at the same time as Dave.
   d. Both *a* and *b*

Comparing and Contrasting

4. Which sentence tells the ways Sam and Dave are the same?
   a. They are both tall.
   b. The boys are adopted, play sports, help each other, and like jokes.
   c. They both have brown eyes.

5. Which sentence tells one way the boys are different?
   a. Sam is younger than Dave.
   b. Dave and Sam are adopted by the same family.
   c. They both play sports.

6. Look at the picture of Dave and Sam. How do they look the same?
   a. Sam and Dave are brothers.
   b. Sam and Dave are adopted.
   c. Sam and Dave are boys.

Comparing and Contrasting 5, *continued*

7. What is one way the boys look different?

    a. Dave has dark skin and Sam has light skin.

    b. Dave and Sam have hair.

    c. Dave likes football.

8. What do the boys do that makes them different?

    a. They are interested in each other's hobbies.

    b. They help each other if they can.

    c. They play different sports and have different hobbies.

9. Sam likes to tease and Dave likes being teased. What part of the story tells about this difference?

    a. The beginning

    b. The middle

    c. The end

Asking Questions

Ask a question to find out how Sam and Dave are alike.

Writing Prompt ••

Brothers and sisters are different. Write the names of the kids in your family at the top of your paper. List the ways you are different from one another. Then list the ways you are the same.

Comparing and Contrasting 6 ·············

Ms. Hyde does something in her class that none of the other teachers do. Once each day, she closes the door. She does not say a word. She puts her hands in the air. Each student knows what to do. For exactly two minutes, the students may do something they like.

Today Ms. Hyde does jumping jacks by her desk. Dan and Clair reach high in the air and then bend down to touch their toes. Jade and Seth go to the board. Jade writes spelling words. Seth does math. Cole puts his headset on and listens to a tape. Kate goes to the easel to draw flowers. Everyone has fun.

Exactly two minutes later, Ms. Hyde stops her jumping jacks. She puts her hands in the air. Her students sit down. No one says a word. Ms. Hyde opens the door. Class starts again. The students know they will have this special time again tomorrow.

Comparing and Contrasting 6, *continued*

Main Idea and Details

1. Which is the best title for this story?
   a. Ms. Hyde Gets Some Exercise
   b. Ms. Hyde's Two-Minute Special
   c. Seth Does Math

2. What is special about the two minutes?
   a. The students can do something they like.
   b. Ms. Hyde does jumping jacks for two minutes.
   c. The students have time to themselves.
   d. All of the above

3. How does Ms. Hyde tell her students it is the special time?
   a. She tells her students what to do.
   b. She closes the door and puts her hands in the air.
   c. She writes the time on the board.

Comparing and Contrasting

4. What are Dan and Claire doing that is the same?
   a. They are doing toe touches.
   b. They are doing math.
   c. Dan and Claire are not doing the same thing.

5. What are Dan and Claire doing that is different?
   a. Dan is touching his toes and Claire is reaching up.
   b. Dan is stretching and Claire is stretching.
   c. Dan and Claire are doing the same thing.

Comparing and Contrasting 6, *continued*

6. How are Jade and Seth doing the same thing?

    a. They are writing with chalk on the board.

    b. They are in the same grade.

    c. Jade is spelling and Seth is doing math.

    d. Both *a* and *c*

7. How is Kate's picture different from Seth's?

    a. Kate's drawing has flowers and Seth's drawing has stars.

    b. Kate is drawing and Seth is drawing.

    c. Seth is counting his fingers and Kate is counting flowers.

8. How is Ms. Hyde's class different from other classes?

    a. Ms. Hyde lets her students do something they like to do every day.

    b. Ms. Hyde teaches class for two minutes.

    c. The students do jumping jacks for two minutes.

Asking Questions

Ask someone from another class how your teachers are the same.

Writing Prompt ••

Write a story that tells what you would do if you had a two-minute special in your classroom every day.

The big day is here. It is the Tenth Annual Pet Show. This is a big event. Over 1,000 people are coming. More than 300 pets are in this show. Ten veterinarians will be the judges.

Mr. Shell is at the show. His sheepdog, Shep, has long black-and-white fur. Shep is sure to win the Big Dog contest. His tricks will get a blue ribbon.

Ben will show his dog, Scoots, for the first time. Scoots is a small dog. He has a short, tan coat. Scoots is not a purebred, but he is friendly. Ben thinks he will win the Nicest Dog contest.

Kay will show her cat and her rabbit. They are both purebred. They win many shows. Kay has competition this year. There are ten cats and 23 rabbits in this show.

Comparing and Contrasting 7, *continued*

Main Idea and Details

1. Which is the best title for this story?

    a. The Tenth Annual Pet Show

    b. Veterinarian Judges

    c. A Rabbit Contest

2. How many people are coming to this pet show?

    a. 1,000

    b. 1,025

    c. Over 1,000

3. How many pets are entered in the show?

    a. More than 300

    b. About 300

    c. 300

4. Who is Mr. Shell?

    a. Ben's neighbor

    b. The man who entered Shep, the sheepdog

    c. One of the judges

5. Which person's animals have won many contests?

    a. Mr. Shell's

    b. Ben's

    c. Kay's

Comparing and Contrasting

6. What is a difference between last year's pet show and this year's show?

    a. Last year's show was bigger.

    b. Last year's show was the ninth and this year's show is the tenth.

    c. There are no differences.

7. What is the difference in the size of the two dogs?

    a. The dogs are the same size.

    b. The dogs are in different contests.

    c. Shep is larger than Scoots.

8. What difference is there in the color of the dogs?

    a. Scoots is tan and Shep is black-and-white.

    b. The dogs both have long fur.

    c. Both *a* and *b*

9. How are Shep and Scoots alike?

    a. They are the same size.

    b. They are both dogs and pets.

    c. They both have long fur.

10. What is the same about Kay's cat and her rabbit?

    a. Both are purebred animals and win lots of ribbons.

    b. Both are white.

    c. Both will have competition.

    d. Both *a* and *c*

Comparing and Contrasting 7, *continued*

Asking Questions

Ask a question to find out how the pet show has changed from the first to the tenth.

Writing Prompt

Copy this chart. Fill it in with the information from the story and what you know about animals.

	Shep	Scoots	Cat	Rabbit
Fur				
Color				
Size				
Talents				
Sound				

Becca is in the choir. She has black pants, a white shirt, and a blue vest. She needs black shoes.

Becca and her sister go to the store. They find four pairs of black shoes. One pair is plain. Another pair has tassels. A third pair has tassels and a fringe trim. The last pair has a fringe trim. The same company makes them.

They look at the prices. The plain pair is $12. The pair with tassels is $13.95. The shoes that cost the most have tassels and a fringe trim. They are $19.95. Becca and her sister talk about how the shoes are the same and different.

Main Idea and Details

1. What is the main idea of this story?

   a. Becca and her sister shop for shoes.

   b. Becca likes black shoes.

   c. Becca gets an outfit for choir.

2. What did Becca find at the store?

   a. She found shoes that were plain.

   b. She found four pairs of black shoes.

   c. She found black shoes that cost a lot of money.

   d. All of the above

3. What was the last thing Becca checked for each pair?

   a. She checked the color.

   b. She checked the price.

   c. She checked the style.

Comparing and Contrasting

4. Which sentence tells how the shoes are the same?

   a. The shoes are black and the same company makes them.

   b. The shoes are the same color and have trim.

   c. The shoes come in many sizes and colors.

5. Which sentence tells how the shoes are different?

   a. Each pair of shoes is a different color.

   b. Each pair of shoes fits Becca.

   c. Each pair of shoes has a different trim and price.

Comparing and Contrasting 8, *continued*

6. What information will Becca use to decide which pair of shoes to buy?

   a. She will pick the style she likes and the price she can pay.

   b. She will pick the style.

   c. She will pick the price she likes.

7. Which sentence tells the information Becca will not use to buy shoes?

   a. She will not use the color or the manufacturer to decide.

   b. She will not use color or size to decide.

   c. She will not use color or price to decide.

Asking Questions

Ask me a question about how the shoes are different.

Writing Prompt ··

Write a paragraph that tells how you made a choice at the store. Did you compare and contrast color, style, and price?

Clear River was a clean, small town. It got its name from the clean, clear river that ran through the middle of town. There was a small grocery store and a gas station. There was one school. There was a little park with swings for the kids.

Some people drove a long way to their jobs. They wished their jobs were closer to home. Others said jobs would help the gas station and grocery store. One lady said she could open a sandwich shop if there were more jobs.

A business owner needed to build a new factory. The factory had to be near a river. He came to Clear River. Everyone was excited. The factory needed workers. People from Clear River could work close to home. The grocery store and gas station would sell more. A new sandwich shop would open.

Ten years went by. Clear River changed. The clear, clean river was dirty. The air was filled with smoke from the factory. A big grocery store put the small store out of business. The park had litter everywhere. There were two more schools. More people lived in Clear River. It was a big town.

Comparing and Contrasting 9, *continued*

Main Idea and Details

1. Which is the best title for this story?

   a. Clear River Changes

   b. Wonderful Changes in Clear River

   c. The Factory Advantage

2. Why did people want a factory in their town?

   a. They wanted their town to get smaller.

   b. They needed a sandwich shop.

   c. They wanted jobs close to home.

3. What made the people excited?

   a. A new factory would be built in Clear River.

   b. A factory had to be near a river.

   c. There was a grocery store.

Comparing and Contrasting

4. Which sentence describes the changes over the last ten years?

   a. There were more schools and people, pollution, a big grocery store, and litter.

   b. There were more jobs and the town prospered.

   c. Both *a* and *b*

5. How did the environment in Clear River change?

   a. The air and water became polluted.

   b. Large stores were built.

   c. There was more litter.

   d. Both *a* and *c*

6. Which sentence describes how Clear River stayed the same?

    a. Clear River did not stay the same after the factory was built.

    b. Clear River had a grocery store, a sandwich shop, and lots of jobs.

    c. Clear River stayed a small town with lots of jobs.

7. Which sentence describes how the factory changed Clear River?

    a. The factory brought new jobs and more business to the town.

    b. The factory polluted the river and the air in Clear River.

    c. Both *a* and *b*

8. How did working people change when the factory came?

    a. People drove shorter distances to work.

    b. People had more time at home because they did not drive a long way to work.

    c. People saved money on gas because they drove less.

    d. All of the above

Asking Questions

Ask a question to learn how the town changed after the factory came.

> **Writing Prompt** ••
>
> Sometimes changes are good. Other changes are not good. List the changes that have happened in your neighborhood over the last several years. Tell whether each change has been a good one.

Ice-skating and inline-skating are both sports you can enjoy all year. No matter which one you like better, they are great exercise.

To enjoy both sports, be sure the boots fit well. If the boots are too tight or too loose, your feet will hurt and skating will not be fun. You need room for your toes. The top of the boot or the cuff should be high enough to support your ankles. Inline-skate boots are usually made of hard plastic, but ice-skate boots are made of leather.

These skates can be expensive. Save money by purchasing high-end, used skates that are in good condition or last year's model when it goes on sale. Find a store with a good reputation and sales people who know the sports. Do your own research before you shop. The Internet is a good tool, but be sure you know what you are doing. Ask an adult to help you make an Internet purchase.

Ice-skate blades have two sharp edges. These edges will keep your feet from sliding out sideways. Inline skates have four wheels. The larger the wheel, the faster you will skate. Remember to start slowly. Always wear protective gear, and expect to spend some time on the ice or the ground.

Comparing and Contrasting 10, *continued*

Main Idea and Details

1. Which is the best title for this story?
   a. The Skating Sports
   b. The Day I Started Skating
   c. It's All About Feet

2. What times of year are best for skating?
   a. You ice-skate only in the winter.
   b. You inline-skate only in the summer.
   c. You can skate all year.

3. What is most important about skate boots?
   a. That they fit comfortably
   b. That the boots are big enough for thick socks
   c. That the boots support your ankles
   d. Both *a* and *c*

Comparing and Contrasting

4. Inline-skating and ice-skating are sports and good types of _____?
   a. Exercise
   b. Recreation
   c. Competition
   d. All of the above

5. How is the fit of the boot for each type of skating the same?
   a. The ice-skate blades should be sharp.
   b. The boots should be made of plastic.
   c. The boots must be comfortable with room for your toes and good ankle support.

6. What are the boots for each kind of skate made of?

   a. Inline skates are harder to wear and ice skates are leather.

   b. Inline skates are made of hard plastic and ice skates are made of leather.

   c. Inline skates protect your feet better than ice skates.

7. How are the prices of inline and ice skates the same?

   a. Both kinds of skates are expensive.

   b. Both kinds of skates are inexpensive.

   c. Both kinds of skates should be expensive to be high quality.

8. What are different ways to save money buying skates?

   a. Buy only what you can afford and hope the skates are good quality.

   b. Find a store with a good reputation.

   c. Buy used skates, buy last year's model on sale, or shop for deals on the Internet.

9. How do inline skates and ice skates move differently?

   a. You can glide with both kinds of skates.

   b. Inline skates move on wheels and ice skates move on blades.

   c. Inline skates require a hard surface and ice skates need ice.

Asking Questions

Ask a question to learn what might happen when you are learning each sport.

Writing Prompt

Write a paragraph about your experiences with inline-skating and ice-skating. Then tell how these experiences were alike.

Exclusion 1

Today is Beth's birthday. Her mom took Beth and three of her friends to a park with rides. They had a blast!

First they rode the roller coaster. They yelled and screamed, but they loved the ride. Peter covered his eyes so he couldn't see. Beth didn't even hold onto the safety bar. Sue was the only one who felt sick on the ride.

After the roller coaster, they tossed balls at targets. Rick and Sue each won a prize, but not Beth or Peter. Then they went to get snacks. Beth got pink cotton candy. The others got hot dogs.

Beth's mom asked her, "Have you had a good time on your birthday?"

"You bet!" Beth said. "This park rocks! Thanks, Mom!"

Exclusion 1, *continued*

Main Idea and Details

1. What is the main idea of this story?
   a. Beth's mom had fun at the park.
   b. Sue got sick on the roller coaster.
   c. Beth and her friends went to a park with rides.

2. Why did Beth's mom take her and her friends to the park?
   a. To celebrate Beth's birthday
   b. To get snacks
   c. To learn to ride a roller coaster

3. What snacks did the children eat?
   a. Hamburgers and cotton candy
   b. Cotton candy and tacos
   c. Hot dogs and cotton candy

Exclusion

4. What didn't the children do at the park?
   a. Ride the Ferris wheel
   b. Toss balls at targets
   c. Ride the roller coaster

5. Who did not feel sick on the roller coaster?
   a. Peter, Beth, and Sue
   b. Rick, Sue, and Beth
   c. Beth, Rick, and Peter

6. Which of these did not win a prize for tossing balls?

   a. Peter

   b. Sue

   c. Rick

7. Which statement is not true?

   a. Beth's dad took her and her friends to the amusement park.

   b. Beth had a great time at the amusement park.

   c. Only one person felt sick on the roller coaster ride.

8. Which of these is not safe to do at an amusement park?

   a. Hold onto the safety bar while you are on a ride.

   b. Stay with your friends or your family.

   c. Stand up on a Ferris wheel ride.

Asking Questions

Ask me a question about Beth's day at the amusement park.

Writing Prompt •

What is your favorite thing to do at an amusement park? Tell what you like to do. Explain what you like most about it.

Jill takes violin lessons. She plays each day. She can't play very well yet. Sometimes she plays squeaks instead of notes.

Max is Jill's dog. He does not like to hear Jill play. It hurts his ears. Max howls and howls. Then Jill can't hear herself play the violin.

Jill got an idea. She got earmuffs from her dresser. She put them on Max. Max could not hear her play. He went to sleep. Now Jill could play in peace.

Exclusion 2, *continued*

Main Idea and Details

1. What is the main idea of this story?

    a. Max plays the violin.

    b. Jill solves a problem.

    c. Jill learns to howl.

2. How well does Jill play the violin?

    a. Very well

    b. Not very well

3. What makes Max howl?

    a. Cleaning his ears

    b. Hearing Jill play the violin

    c. Wearing earmuffs

Exclusion

4. Which statement is not true?

    a. Max does not play the violin.

    b. Jill plays the violin.

    c. Max and Jill play the violin.

5. Why doesn't Max like to hear Jill play the violin?

    a. It hurts his eyes.

    b. It hurts his tail.

    c. It hurts his ears.

6. Why didn't Jill want Max to howl?

   a. So she could hear herself play.

   b. So she could see herself play.

   c. So she could sing to herself.

7. Which statement is not true?

   a. Jill had a good idea.

   b. Max did not mind the earmuffs.

   c. Max had a good idea.

8. What could Jill try if the earmuffs didn't work?

   a. Keep Max out of the room.

   b. Put socks on Max's ears.

   c. Howl at Max.

Asking Questions

Ask me a question about playing a violin.

Writing Prompt

It's not easy to learn to play a violin. It takes a lot of practice.

Think about something you can do that wasn't easy to learn. What was hard at first? How did you learn to do it better? Write about how you learned something that wasn't easy at first.

Exclusion 3 ·······································

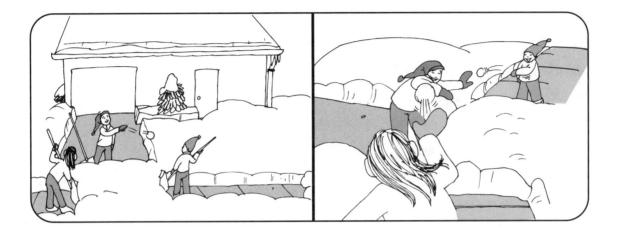

There was a big snow storm last night. Three feet of snow are on the ground. School is closed today.

Kim, Mark, and Ted slept late this morning. After breakfast, Dad asked them to shovel snow. "You can play outside after you shovel," he said. "Please shovel the driveway and the sidewalk first, though."

The children got busy right away. Mark shoveled the driveway. Kim and Ted worked on the sidewalk. The sun was shining. It wasn't very cold.

When they were almost done, Mark threw a snowball at Ted. "Catch this!" he shouted.

Ted laughed. He said, "Here is one for you!"

They all joined in the fight. Then Dad came outside. The children had not finished shoveling. They thought Dad would be mad. But Dad surprised them. He said, "You kids have worked hard. I'll finish this up. Have a great time in the snow!"

Exclusion 3, *continued*

Main Idea and Details

1. What is the main idea of this story?
    a. What the children did on a snowy day
    b. How the blizzard came to town
    c. Why school was closed today

2. How much snow fell overnight?
    a. Two feet
    b. Three feet
    c. Four feet

3. Who started a snowball fight?
    a. Ted
    b. Mark
    c. Dad

Exclusion

4. Why wasn't school open today?
    a. There was too much rain.
    b. It was too windy.
    c. There was too much snow.

5. Which statement is not true?
    a. The children woke up early today.
    b. The children slept late today.
    c. The children ate breakfast before they shoveled snow.

6. Who did not shovel the sidewalk?

    a. Ted

    b. Kim

    c. Mark

7. Which statement is not false?

    a. It was bitter cold outside.

    b. It was very warm outside.

    c. It was not very cold outside.

8. Which statement is not true?

    a. Dad was angry that the children didn't finish shoveling.

    b. Dad said he would finish doing the shoveling.

    c. Dad was glad the children were having fun in the snow.

Asking Questions

Ask me a question about the children.

Writing Prompt •

Sometimes the weather is so bad that schools have to close.
Imagine you are a weather forecaster. Write a weather forecast
that would make schools close for the day.

Pat loves science. She wants to be a scientist when she grows up. Her dad gave her a science kit for her birthday. Pat could not wait to try an experiment. She would make shampoo. It would make her hair soft and shiny. Everyone would want some of her shampoo.

Pat knew that chemicals could be dangerous. She put goggles on to protect her eyes. Then she mixed some chemicals to make her shampoo. She poured in something green to give it a nice color. She added some liquid soap to make it foamy. Then she added olive oil. She put some perfume in to make it smell nice.

As soon as the shampoo was ready, Pat used it to wash her hair. Then she dried her hair with a towel. Next she would comb it.

Pat looked in the mirror. What a shock! Her hair was falling out! Clump by clump, all her hair fell out. She was bald!

Poor Pat! She packed up her science kit and threw it away. "I still like science," she thought, "but I won't try it at home again. This was not fun!"

Exclusion 4, *continued*

Main Idea and Details

1. Which is the best title for this story?

    a. Pat Washes Her Hair

    b. Pat's Experiment

    c. Pat Wears Goggles

2. What did Pat's dad give her for her birthday?

    a. A science kit

    b. New shampoo

    c. Tickets for a movie

3. What was Pat's first experiment with the science kit?

    a. Making soap

    b. Making shampoo

    c. Making perfume

Exclusion

4. Which statement is not true?

    a. Pat does not like science.

    b. Pat had a birthday last week.

    c. Pat did not make a good shampoo.

5. Why did Pat wear goggles to mix her shampoo?

    a. So her hair would not cover her eyes

    b. So she could see what she was doing

    c. So no chemicals would get into her eyes

6. Why did Pat add perfume to her shampoo?

   a. So the shampoo would not have a bad smell

   b. So the shampoo would not have a bad color

   c. So her hair would not be hard to comb

7. Which statement is not true?

   a. Pat was pleased with her shampoo.

   b. Pat did not keep her science kit.

   c. The shampoo was not good for Pat's hair.

8. What does a completely bald head look like?

   a. Just a little hair on the head

   b. No hair on the head

   c. Lots of hair on the head

Asking Questions

Ask me a question about Pat's experiment.

Writing Prompt ••

Think about how Pat felt when her hair fell out. Write a letter to her.
Tell her how you feel about what happened to her.

Exclusion 5 ·····································

Today is Saturday. It is Seth's favorite day of the week. On Saturdays, Seth wakes up bright and early. He gets dressed and makes his bed. Then he gets some cereal. Seth's dad sleeps late, so Seth tries to be quiet.

Seth puts his cereal on a tray. He takes it into the den. He watches some cartoons. Then he plays a video game or two.

Seth's dad gets up in time to make lunch. Then they do errands. The best errand is going to the hardware store. Seth's dad tells him all about tools and hardware.

Seth is helping his dad build a tree house. They work on it every Saturday afternoon. Soon the tree house will be finished. Then Seth will have one more reason to love Saturdays. He can invite a friend to climb up to the tree house with him.

Exclusion 5, *continued*

Main Idea and Details

1. What is the main idea of this story?

    a. Seth fixes breakfast for himself.

    b. Seth's dad, a great builder

    c. Saturday, Seth's favorite day of the week

2. What does Seth fix for breakfast on Saturdays?

    a. Toast and jelly

    b. Cereal

    c. Fruit and rolls

3. What is Seth's favorite errand?

    a. Going to the grocery store

    b. Going to the lumberyard

    c. Going to the hardware store

Exclusion

4. Which statement is not true?

    a. Seth's dad gets up early on Saturdays.

    b. Seth does not sleep late on Saturdays.

    c. Seth does not fix lunch for his dad.

5. Why does Seth try to be quiet on Saturday mornings?

    a. He doesn't like noise.

    b. He doesn't want to wake up his dad.

    c. He doesn't want to scare himself.

6. Why does Seth carry his cereal on a tray?

    a. The bowl is too hot to touch.

    b. The cereal is too heavy.

    c. He doesn't want to spill anything on the floor.

7. Which weather wouldn't Seth want for the next few Saturdays?

    a. Stormy and windy

    b. Sunny and mild

    c. Cloudy and warm

8. Why do you think Seth doesn't build the tree house by himself?

Asking Questions

Ask me a question about what Seth does on Saturdays.

Writing Prompt ••

Seth has a Saturday routine that he likes. Write what you would like as your Saturday routine. Tell all the things you would do.

Mrs. Wong lives by herself. She has been a widow for ten years. She is over eighty, but she takes good care of herself. She exercises often. She goes for walks around the neighborhood.

Everyone likes Mrs. Wong. She is always friendly. She often bakes things for her neighbors. When she sees a lemonade stand, she always buys at least one glass of lemonade. She is just that kind of a person.

Today people are worried about Mrs. Wong. They haven't seen her for three days. She hasn't picked up the papers on her porch. Mr. Lark stopped by her house on his way to work. He rang the bell and waited. After a while, Mrs. Wong opened the door.

"Hi, Mrs. Wong," said Mr. Lark. "We've been worried about you. Are you okay?"

"Yes, thank you," Mrs. Wong smiled. "I've had a bad cold, but I'm much better today. You are so kind to check on me. I'll have to make you some special brownies!"

Exclusion 6, *continued*

Main Idea and Details

1. What is the main idea of this story?

    a. Good neighbors

    b. A Lemonade Stand

    c. Mrs. Wong helps Mr. Lark

2. How does Mrs. Wong stay in good health?

    a. She takes walks.

    b. She takes lots of medicines.

    c. She exercises.

    d. Both *a* and *c*

3. What does Mrs. Wong do when she walks by a lemonade stand?

    a. She turns her head and walks right by it.

    b. She buys some lemonade.

    c. She asks for a glass of water.

Exclusion

4. How do you know that Mrs. Wong doesn't have a husband?

    a. The story doesn't mention her husband.

    b. She is a widow.

    c. She was never married.

5. Why were Mrs. Wong's neighbors worried about her?

    a. No one knew where her husband was.

    b. No one had seen her for days.

    c. No one had seen her for three weeks.

6. What did the neighbors notice about Mrs. Wong's front porch?

    a. She hadn't watered her flowers.

    b. She hadn't picked up her newspapers.

    c. She hadn't changed her flag.

7. Which statement is true?

    a. Mrs. Wong was not glad to see Mr. Lark.

    b. Mrs. Wong had not had a bad cold.

    c. Mrs. Wong did not answer the door right away.

8. Why hadn't Mrs. Wong seen her neighbors for a few days?

    a. She didn't like to see her neighbors.

    b. She was not home for a few days.

    c. She wasn't feeling well.

Asking Questions

Ask me a question about a lemonade stand.

Writing Prompt •••

Write a list of things that make a good neighbor. Then use your list to write a paragraph that describes a good neighbor.

Exclusion 7

Leah likes to cook with her mom. Her mom helps her make dinner every other night. There are six people in Leah's family. They all like to eat what Leah cooks.

Today Leah will make pepperoni pizza. First she mixes the dough. She adds water to the yeast. Then she mixes it with flour to make dough. She kneads the dough until it is smooth. Then she lets the dough rise.

Next Leah spreads the dough onto a pizza pan. Her mom shows her how to stretch the dough to the edge of the pan. Then Leah pours pizza sauce on top of the dough. She spreads it evenly. She makes sure the sauce doesn't touch the edge of the dough. Next Leah puts pepperoni slices around the pizza. Then she covers the pizza with grated cheese.

Meanwhile, her mom heats the oven for the pizza. When the pizza is ready, Mom puts it in the oven. She wears oven mitts to protect her hands.

The pizza bakes for twenty minutes. Leah fixes a tossed salad while the pizza bakes. Then the whole family gathers at the dinner table to enjoy Leah's dinner. Leah's family is very glad she likes to cook!

Exclusion 7, *continued*

Main Idea and Details

1. What is the main idea of this story?

   a. Why Leah cooks for her family

   b. Leah's family likes pizza and salad.

   c. Leah likes to cook for her family.

2. How often does Leah cook?

   a. Every night

   b. Twice a week

   c. More than twice a week

3. Which part of the pizza did Leah make from scratch?

   a. The pizza dough

   b. The pizza pan

   c. The pizza sauce

Exclusion

4. Which statement is not true?

   a. There are seven people in Leah's family.

   b. There are six people in Leah's family.

   c. There are five people in Leah's family besides Leah.

5. Which statement is true?

   a. Leah's family doesn't like her cooking.

   b. Leah doesn't like cooking for her family.

   c. Leah doesn't cook by herself.

6. Which topping didn't Leah put on her pizza?

    a. Pepperoni

    b. Sausage

    c. Cheese

7. Who didn't put the pizza in the oven?

    a. Mom

    b. Leah

8. Why did Leah's mom use oven mitts?

    a. So she wouldn't burn the pizza

    b. So her hands wouldn't burn

    c. So she wouldn't scratch the pizza

Asking Questions

Ask me a question about baking pizza.

Writing Prompt •

Do you like to eat pizza? Write directions to make your favorite pizza.

Jake lived on a farm in the country. The farms in the area were all large, so Jake's family didn't have any neighbors nearby. Jake had to spend lots of time doing chores to help on the farm, but he also had time to do whatever he wanted.

One beautiful spring day, Jake decided to fly his kite. There was just enough wind to get it going easily. Jake knew the perfect spot to fly his kite. He would go to the south pasture. There were no cattle there right now, and there was a lot of open space with no trees.

Jake made sure his kite was in good shape for flying. He checked the knots to make sure they were tight enough. He checked the spool of string to make sure there were no tangles. Then it was time to launch the kite. Jake faced the wind and began running with the kite behind him. In no time, the kite was aloft. It soared into the air.

As Jake let out more and more string, his kite ascended higher and higher. What a fantastic flight! Jake wished he could share the fun with a friend. He decided that was exactly what he would do. He would invite some of his friends over to fly kites together on Saturday. If the weather was good, they would have a great time.

Main Idea and Details

1. What is the main idea of this story?

    a. Jake flies a kite.

    b. Jake does his chores.

    c. Jake likes the weather.

2. In what season does this story take place?

    a. Summer

    b. Fall

    c. Winter

    d. Spring

3. What kind of animals does Jake's family raise on their farm?

    a. Buffalo

    b. Cattle

    c. Horses

Exclusion

4. Which statement is not true?

    a. Jake did not have any free time.

    b. Jake had many chores to do.

    c. Jake did not have neighbors nearby.

5. Which kind of day would not be good for flying a kite?

    a. A calm, sunny day with no wind

    b. A cloudy, windy day with rain showers

    c. A fair day with some wind

    d. Both *a* and *b*

6. Why did Jake choose a spot with no trees?

   a. So no birds would get in the way of his kite

   b. So his kite wouldn't get caught in a tree

   c. So a tree wouldn't drop any fruit or twigs on him

7. What might have happened if Jake had not checked his kite before he flew it?

   a. A knot might have loosened.

   b. The kite might have been broken.

   c. Both *a* and *b*

8. Where would not be a good place to fly a kite where you live? Explain why that would not be a good spot to fly a kite.

Asking Questions

Ask me a question about where Jake lived.

Writing Prompt ·····························

Jake flew his kite when he had some free time. Write about one thing you like to do with your free time.

Mrs. Lee loves to sew. Every year she makes Halloween costumes for her family. She works hard to make the costumes special. There is a Halloween party in the park. The Lees wear their costumes to the party. This year they dressed up like insects and a spider. They won a prize for the best costumes. Mrs. Lee was proud.

Main Idea and Details

1. What is the main idea of this story?

    a. Mr. Lee dressed up like a spider.

    b. Mrs. Lee works hard.

    c. Mrs. Lee makes Halloween costumes.

2. Where was the Halloween party?

    a. At the Lee's home

    b. In the park

    c. At the school

3. What did the Lee family dress up as this year?

    a. Caterpillars and a snake

    b. Fish and a bug

    c. Insects and a spider

Exclusion

4. Which statement is not true?

    a. Mrs. Lee likes to sew.

    b. Mrs. Lee doesn't work hard.

5. Which costume would not be an insect?

    a. Wasp

    b. Turtle

    c. Fly

6. Which statement is true?

   a. Mrs. Lee did not make a pumpkin costume this year.

   b. Mrs. Lee did not make a ladybug costume this year.

   c. Mrs. Lee did not make a butterfly costume this year.

7. What did not happen at the party in the park?

   a. Mrs. Lee sewed Halloween costumes.

   b. The Lees wore their insect costumes.

   c. The Lees won a prize for their costumes.

8. What shouldn't Mr. Lee say to Mrs. Lee about the costumes?

   a. Thank you for making our costumes.

   b. I don't like our costumes.

   c. You sew very well.

Asking Questions

Ask me a question that isn't about Mrs. Lee.

Writing Prompt ···

Imagine that someone will make a costume for you. Write what your costume would look like. Then write where you would wear your costume and where you would not wear your costume.

Timothy hopped on his skateboard and headed for the zoo. Little did he know what an adventure he would have there!

Just as Timothy reached the zoo entrance, his skateboard lifted him right off the ground. He grabbed the front to keep his balance. He heard a flapping noise behind him. Sure enough, his skateboard had grown wings! "Yikes!" he thought. "I'd better sit down until I get the hang of this."

It was easier to balance sitting down, but Timothy couldn't control his skateboard. Soon the skateboard flew him over a large pool—with hungry sharks in it! Timothy thought he could steer the skateboard better if he stood up. That is just what he did. The more he practiced steering the skateboard, the better the skateboard worked. "This is awesome!" Timothy cried.

Things went well until Timothy saw a giraffe eating leaves from tall trees. Timothy tried to fly close to the giraffe's head. Instead he crashed right through the top of a tree. Whomp! He landed on the ground beside the giraffe. She licked his face with her large tongue.

"Wake up, Timothy!" he heard his mom say. "Time for school, Timothy. Why is your bed such a mess? Your sheets are all over the place."

"Well, I'm sorry about the mess," Timothy said, "but you wouldn't believe the great dream I just had!"

Main Idea and Details

1. Which is the best title for this story?
    a. Timothy's Horror Story
    b. Timothy's Great Dream
    c. Timothy's Messy Bed

2. Where was Timothy going when he first got on his skateboard?
    a. To the skateboard park
    b. To the aquarium
    c. To the zoo

3. Why did Timothy sit down on his flying skateboard?
    a. To get a better view
    b. To get his balance
    c. To see if he could stop the skateboard

Exclusion

4. How do you know that Timothy's skateboard didn't really fly?
    a. Skateboards can't fly.
    b. Timothy was dreaming it all.
    c. Timothy was too young to fly a skateboard.
    d. Both *a* and *b*

5. Why did Timothy fly over sharks in a pool?
    a. He wanted to feed the sharks.
    b. He couldn't steer the skateboard.
    c. He didn't think the sharks were dangerous.

6. Which statement is true?

   a. Practice did not help Timothy steer the skateboard.

   b. Timothy did not steer the skateboard well without practice.

   c. Timothy did not learn how to steer the skateboard.

7. Why did Timothy and the skateboard crash into a tree?

   a. Timothy wasn't watching where he was steering the skateboard.

   b. The skateboard was busy trying to watch the giraffe.

   c. Both *a* and *b*

8. Which statement is not true?

   a. Timothy's sheets were a mess after the dream.

   b. Timothy did not enjoy the dream.

   c. Timothy's mom woke him up from his dream.

Asking Questions

Ask me a question about Timothy's dream.

Writing Prompt •

Suppose Timothy's dream really happened. Imagine you are a news reporter. Write about what happened at the zoo. Remember to include the answers to these questions in your report:

Who?

What?

When?

Where?

Why or How?

Problem Solving 1 ·····························

Jen got new skates as a gift and she couldn't wait to try them. Her mom said she needed a helmet and pads. She told Jen she couldn't skate until she got them. Jen knew she couldn't get those things until the weekend. She did not want to wait that long.

One afternoon Jen's mom was taking a nap. Jen sneaked outside. She walked down to the path behind her house and put on her skates. She just wanted to try them out for a minute. Jen stood up and started to move. She lost her balance and fell hard to the ground. Her wrist really hurt. Jen started to cry.

Problem Solving 1, *continued*

Main Idea and Details

1. Which is a better title for this story?

   a. Jen's New Helmet

   b. Jen Takes a Fall

2. Where did Jen go skating?

   a. In the park

   b. On the driveway

   c. On the path

3. What was Jen doing at the end of the story?

   a. Crying

   b. Skating

   c. Asking for help

Problem Solving

4. Why wouldn't Jen's mom let her go skating?

   a. Jen didn't know how to skate.

   b. Jen needed a helmet and pads.

   c. Jen shouldn't skate alone.

5. What pads do you wear when you skate?

   a. Wrist, knee, and elbow

   b. Shoulder, elbow, and knee

   c. Wrist, shoulder, and knee

6. Why did Jen fall down so easily?

   a. She wasn't wearing a helmet.

   b. The path was slippery.

   c. She wasn't used to her new skates.

7. Jen hurt her wrist in the fall. What other problem will she have to solve?

   a. She needs to get her skates off.

   b. Her mom will be mad at her.

   c. She still needs to get a helmet.

8. Who could Jen have asked to help her learn how to skate?

   a. A parent or other adult

   b. A friend who already knows how to skate

   c. Both *a* and *b*

Asking Questions

Ask me a question about skating.

Writing Prompt •

What are some safety rules to follow when you are skating or riding a bicycle?

Problem Solving 2 ·····························

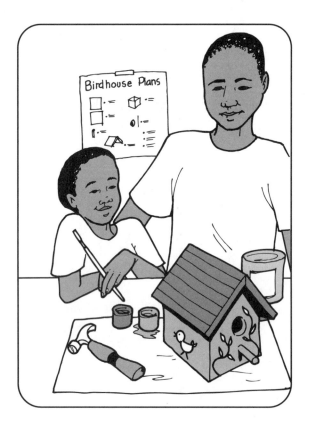

Collis wants to make something special for show and tell. He knows his dad can make all kinds of things. He asks, "Dad, can you help me? I want to make something. I want to take it to show and tell."

"Sure, Collis," his dad says. "We can make a birdhouse."

"That sounds great," says Collis. "I don't know how to make a birdhouse, though."

"That's okay," says his dad. "I'll cut out the pieces. Then you can help me put it together. I'll let you do all the painting."

They worked together on the birdhouse. Collis learned a lot about how to build something. His favorite part was painting the birdhouse.

Problem Solving 2, *continued*

Main Idea and Details

1. What is the main idea of this story?
    a. Collis and his dad build a birdhouse.
    b. Collis takes a birdhouse to show and tell.

2. What did Collis make?
    a. Something out of wood
    b. Something out of metal
    c. Something out of paper

3. Who helped Collis make the birdhouse?
    a. His mom
    b. No one
    c. His dad

Problem Solving

4. Why was it a good idea for Collis's dad to cut out the pieces for the birdhouse?
    a. Collis is too little to use a saw.
    b. Collis doesn't know where the saw is kept.
    c. Collis is supposed to paint the birdhouse.

5. Why was Collis's dad a good person to help him?
    a. He knows how to make things.
    b. He is a bird expert.
    c. He is a professional birdhouse maker.

6. What two materials are you sure Collis and his dad used?

   a. Glue and paint

   b. Wood and paint

   c. Glue and wood

7. During what part of the project did Collis and his dad work together?

   a. Cutting out the pieces

   b. Putting the pieces together

   c. Painting the birdhouse

8. What's something else Collis and his dad could have made out of wood?

   a. Paper airplane

   b. Bird feeder

   c. Bird bath

Asking Questions

Ask me a question about making something with wood.

Writing Prompt ••

What's something you like to do on a rainy day? Tell what you do and why you like it.

Problem Solving 3 ·····························

Darla and her dad were in a boat race. It was a cardboard boat race. They made their boat out of boxes. It took them a week to make their boat. Darla painted it bright blue. She put dolphins on it.

The boat race was at Rock Creek Park. There is a shallow pond at the park. It is only about two feet deep. Darla and her dad were having fun in the race. They rowed their boat on the pond. Halfway across, they had trouble. Their boat soaked up too much water. It sank to the bottom of the pond. Darla and her dad laughed. They had fun wading through the water. They waved to the other boaters. They had a great time!

Problem Solving 3, *continued*

Main Idea and Details

1. Which is a better title for this story?
   a. Fun with a Sinking Boat
   b. Building a Cardboard Boat

2. Where was the boat race held?
   a. Rock Creek Park
   b. On Rock Creek
   c. Rock Creek Lake

3. What happened to Darla and her dad's cardboard boat?
   a. It came in first place.
   b. It sank.
   c. It was pulled out of the water.

Problem Solving

4. Why was this race held on a shallow pond?
   a. So the boats would go faster
   b. So no one would get hurt when a boat sank
   c. Because everyone is able to swim

5. Why isn't cardboard used to make all boats?
   a. It's too expensive.
   b. It soaks up water.
   c. It's hard to paint.

6. Why were Darla and her dad happy at the end of the story?

    a. They won the race.

    b. They liked their boat.

    c. They were having fun in the water.

7. Which one of these people might have helped Darla and her dad build a better boat?

    a. Architect

    b. Carpenter

    c. Mechanic

8. Do you agree or disagree with this sentence? Explain your answer.

    Darla and her dad were sad that they didn't win the race.

    a. Disagree; they had fun waving to other people in the race.

    b. Agree; they worked hard on the boat and wanted to win.

    c. Disagree; they knew they never had a chance to win.

Asking Questions

Ask me a question about being in a race.

Writing Prompt •

List three things you could make with a huge cardboard box.
Describe each one.

Problem Solving 4 ·····························

It is a rainy day. Matt and his friends want to play a board game. They decide to play Thunder Road. It's a car racing game. Matt opens the box. He starts to set up the board. He notices there are no instructions with the game. None of them have ever played the game before.

Matt's friend Lisa asks, "Why don't we just play another game? Find something we know how to play."

"But this looks cool," says Matt. "I'm sure we can figure something out."

Problem Solving 4, *continued*

Main Idea and Details

1. What is the main idea of this story?

    a. Matt and his friends play Thunder Road.

    b. Matt and his friends try to play a game.

2. What were Matt and his friends going to do?

    a. Go outside and play

    b. Play a board game

    c. Play a card game

3. What is the name of the board game Matt wants to play?

    a. Road Rally

    b. Thunder Rally

    c. Thunder Road

Problem Solving

4. What problem do Matt and his friends have?

    a. It is raining outside.

    b. There are no instructions to the game.

    c. They don't know how to play.

    d. Both *b* and *c*

5. What is Lisa's solution to the problem?

    a. Choose another game to play.

    b. Watch TV.

    c. Don't play the game.

6. Why doesn't Matt want to find another game to play?

    a. He thinks Thunder Road is a cool game.

    b. He wants to make Lisa mad.

    c. He always wants to be in charge.

7. Which of these solutions do you think Matt would choose?

    a. Choose another game to play.

    b. Make up his own rules for Thunder Road.

    c. Decide not to play a game.

8. What wouldn't be a good thing to play instead of Thunder Road?

    a. Video game

    b. Baseball

    c. Card game

Asking Questions

Ask me a question about playing a board game.

Writing Prompt ••

Write about your favorite board game. Tell why you like it the best.

Problem Solving 5 ··································

Dan thinks about dogs all the time. He keeps begging his parents to let him get a dog. They keep telling him the same thing. They say, "Dan, we are hardly ever home. The dog would be alone a lot. That wouldn't be fair to it. Besides, our apartment is much too small for a dog."

Dan knows they are right, but he would still love to get a dog. He doesn't have any brothers or sisters to play with, and a dog would make a great best friend. Dan can't wait until he grows up so he can have his own dog in his own place. Until then, he'll just keep reading about dogs and thinking about what it will be like to have one.

Problem Solving 5, *continued*

Main Idea and Details

1. What is the main idea of this story?

   a. Dan wants to get a dog.

   b. Dan and his parents are rarely home.

2. Where do Dan and his family live?

   a. In a house

   b. In a trailer

   c. In an apartment

3. How many brothers does Dan have?

   a. None

   b. One

   c. Two

Problem Solving

4. What is Dan's problem?

   a. His parents won't talk about getting a dog.

   b. He really wants a dog but can't get one.

   c. He wants to visit his friend who has a dog.

5. Why won't Dan's parents get him a dog?

   a. The dog would be left alone a lot.

   b. Their apartment is too small.

   c. Both *a* and *b*

6. How is Dan dealing with his problem?

   a. He reads and thinks about dogs.

   b. He argues with his parents.

   c. He walks other people's dogs.

7. Which two pets might Dan be able to get instead of a dog?

   a. Goldfish

   b. Horse

   c. Hamster

8. When will Dan be able to get a dog?

   a. When his family moves.

   b. When he grows up and gets his own place.

   c. When his parents get tired of his begging.

Asking Questions

Ask me a question about owning a dog.

Writing Prompt •

Pretend you are a dog living in a small apartment. What are the good and bad things about where you live?

Rick is at the movies with his mom and brother Trey. He is not having a good time. In fact, he is having a terrible time. Rick wanted to see "Spy School." His brother Trey wanted to see "Fright House." Their mom decided that it was Trey's turn to choose. Now Rick is mad. He has to watch a movie he didn't want to see.

Rick's mom is not happy with him, either. She has warned him twice to stop complaining. Now he has decided to just sit and not watch the movie. He'd rather sip his soda and pout. He gets even madder when he looks at Trey. His brother is happily munching his popcorn and acting like nothing is wrong. Rick hopes this movie goes by quickly so he can go back home.

Problem Solving 6, *continued*

Main Idea and Details

1. Which is a better title for this story?

    a. Rick Pouts While Trey Munches

    b. Trey Chooses the Movie

2. Where does this story take place?

    a. At home

    b. In a movie theater

    c. In a car

3. How many times has Rick's mom warned him to stop complaining?

    a. Twice

    b. Three times

    c. Four times

Problem Solving

4. What is the problem in this story?

    a. Rick does not like the movie Trey chose.

    b. The movie Rick chose was sold out.

    c. Rick and Trey's mom does not like the movie.

5. What is Rick doing about the problem?

    a. Enjoying the movie

    b. Pouting and complaining

    c. Leaving the theater

6. What's a better way Rick might handle this problem?

   a. Tell Trey how much he hates the movie.

   b. Try to enjoy the movie and look forward to the next time when he gets to choose.

   c. Both *a* and *b*

7. What is most likely to happen to Rick if he keeps complaining?

   a. His mom will punish him.

   b. Trey will ask him to be quiet.

   c. He will get his way.

8. How do you think Trey feels about the way Rick is acting? Explain your answer.

   a. He doesn't care.

   b. He wishes Rick would stop acting like a baby.

   c. He wishes Rick would have stayed home.

Asking Questions

Ask me a question about going to the movies.

Writing Prompt •

What do you think the movie "Spy School" is about? What do you think the movie "Fright House" is about?

David got hurt during the first baseball practice of the season. He broke his leg. He was sliding into second base when it happened. His foot got caught on the base. He was very sad that he couldn't play baseball all summer. David still went to every practice, though. He liked to watch his friends play.

Before the first game started, the coach walked over to him. "David," he said, "I think you can still help us." The coach gave him a cap that said "Scorekeeper" on it. He also gave him a score book. He said, "I want you to keep the score book for all of our games."

David still wished he could play baseball. Being the scorekeeper, though, would be the next best thing.

Problem Solving 7, *continued*

Main Idea and Details

1. What is the main idea of this story?

    a. David breaks his leg but still helps the team.

    b. David is sad about breaking his leg.

2. What was David doing when he broke his leg?

    a. Sliding into home

    b. Diving to catch a ball

    c. Sliding into second base

3. What did it say on the hat the coach gave to David?

    a. Broken Leg

    b. Second Base

    c. Scorekeeper

Problem Solving

4. How is David going to help the team?

    a. Bring them water

    b. Help carry equipment

    c. Keep the score book

5. Is David completely happy with being the scorekeeper? Why?

    a. No; he's glad to help, but he'd rather be playing.

    b. No; he thinks keeping score will be boring.

    c. Yes; he would rather keep score than play.

6. What caused David's leg to break when he slid into second?

   a. He slid into someone else.

   b. His foot got caught on the base.

   c. The base was loose.

7. What is David's problem in this story?

   a. He broke his leg and can't play baseball.

   b. He doesn't know how to keep score.

   c. He doesn't like his new cap.

8. What is something else David could do to help his team?

   a. Cheer for them at the games.

   b. Stay home and feel sorry for himself.

   c. Both *a* and *b*

Asking Questions

Ask me a question about baseball.

Writing Prompt •••

Pretend you are David's friend and he has just broken his leg. Write him a get-well note.

Problem Solving 8 ·······························

Maureen is so excited. She is getting new glasses. Her mom tells her that she can pick out her own glasses. She tells Maureen how much she can spend. Then she lets her go into the store alone.

The salesperson shows Maureen several frames. Maureen tries each one on and looks at herself in the mirror. "It's so hard to choose," she says to the salesperson. "I don't know which ones to get."

"The ones you have on look very nice," the salesperson says. Maureen takes them off. She looks at the price tag. They are fifty dollars more than she can spend.

"I do like them," Maureen says, "but I think I need something that fits in my price range."

Problem Solving 8, *continued*

Main Idea and Details

1. What is the main idea of this story?

   a. Maureen shops for new glasses.

   b. Maureen doesn't have enough money.

2. Why is Maureen excited?

   a. She knows how much money she can spend.

   b. Her mom dropped her off at the store.

   c. She gets to pick out her own glasses.

3. What did Maureen do after she tried on each pair of glasses?

   a. Looked in the mirror

   b. Looked at the price tag

   c. Looked at the salesperson

Problem Solving

4. Who is helping Maureen make her decision?

   a. Her mom

   b. The salesperson

   c. The eye doctor

5. Why doesn't Maureen get the glasses she really likes?

   a. They don't fit correctly.

   b. She needs to talk to her mom about them.

   c. They are too expensive.

6. Why is it important to buy glasses that you like?

   a. They need to be in your price range.

   b. You will wear them for a long time.

   c. There are many different kinds to choose from.

   d. Both *a* and *b*

7. What could the salesperson do to help Maureen make a good decision?

   a. Only show Maureen frames she can afford.

   b. Let Maureen try on every frame in the store.

   c. Have Maureen's mom come into the store to help.

8. What could Maureen do if she can't decide which glasses to get? Explain your answer.

   a. Find her mom and ask her opinion.

   b. Get contact lenses instead.

   c. Wait a few months and try again.

Asking Questions

Ask me a question about wearing glasses.

Writing Prompt •••

What are some bad things about wearing glasses? What are some good things about wearing glasses?

Readability 3.7

Max and Frank are twins. They do almost everything alike. They look alike, they walk alike, and they even like the same foods. There is one thing that they do that isn't the same. Max is a great singer. Frank, on the other hand, can barely carry a tune.

Frank loves to hear Max sing. There are times, though, when he gets jealous. Max is a professional singer. He has performed with the city symphony. He has also sung with several bands. Frank thinks there's nothing special about him. He thinks Max gets a lot more attention.

Frank likes to think that everything about them should be the same. He knows, though, that Max will always be known as "the singer." Luckily, Max does not let all the attention go to his head. Max is just a regular kid. No matter how famous he gets, Max knows Frank will always be his twin brother and best friend.

Main Idea and Details

1. What is the main idea of this story?

    a. Max and Frank are twins with a difference.

    b. Frank is a very popular singer.

2. Who has Max performed with?

    a. The city symphony

    b. A church choir

    c. Both *a* and *b*

3. What does Max think about all the attention he gets?

    a. He thinks he's very special.

    b. He is embarrassed by it.

    c. He doesn't let it go to his head.

Problem Solving

4. What is Frank's problem?

    a. He wishes he could sing.

    b. He wants to look just like his brother.

    c. He is sometimes jealous of his brother.

5. Why does Frank get jealous of his brother?

    a. He wants to sing like him.

    b. He doesn't like the attention his brother gets.

    c. He doesn't like the way his brother sings.

6. What belief does Frank have that might cause problems?

    a. Max and he should have separate interests.

    b. Everything about the twins should be the same.

    c. Frank should be happy for everything that happens to Max.

7. What does Frank think will happen if Max gets famous?

    a. Max might forget about Frank.

    b. Frank and Max will still be best friends.

    c. Max might not want to talk to Frank.

    d. Both *a* and *c*

8. What might Frank do when he feels jealous about his brother? Explain your answer.

    a. Try to ignore how he feels.

    b. Find someone to talk to about his feelings.

    c. Stop talking to Max until he feels better.

Asking Questions

Ask me a question about twins.

Writing Prompt •

Would you like to have an identical twin? Why?

Maggie needs to write a report on Antarctica. It is for a group project. She promised her team she would have it done tomorrow morning. It just turned eight o'clock and she is only getting started. Maggie's bedtime is nine o'clock. She knows it will take at least two hours to do her report. She is also very tired and can hardly keep her eyes open.

She planned to write her report right after school. When she walked in the door, though, the phone rang. Her friend Sheena was calling. She invited Maggie out for pizza. Maggie's mom said she could go. Maggie had not told her mom about the report. Maggie told her mom that she didn't have any homework. Now she knows she probably won't get the report done tonight. Her team will not get the project finished on time.

Problem Solving 10, continued

Main Idea and Details

1. What is the main idea of this story?
   a. Maggie writes a report on Antarctica.
   b. Maggie goes out with a friend instead of studying.

2. Where did Maggie go after school?
   a. To a movie
   b. To do her homework
   c. Out for pizza

3. Why does Maggie need to write a report on Antarctica?
   a. For a group project
   b. Because her class is studying penguins
   c. It's an interesting place.

Problem Solving

4. What is Maggie's problem?
   a. She does not like the group she was assigned to.
   b. She does not have enough time or energy to do her report.
   c. She went out for pizza with Sheena.

5. Why doesn't Maggie have enough time to do her report?
   a. She lied to her mom.
   b. She went out for pizza with Sheena.
   c. She got the assignment late.

6. How could Maggie have prevented her problem?

    a. She could have turned down Sheena's invitation.

    b. She could ask her mom to work on her report.

    c. She could tell someone on the team the report will be late.

7. What would be the worst way to handle the problem?

    a. Tell her team members that no one told her to do the report.

    b. Tell her mom the truth and ask for her help.

    c. Tell her teacher the truth about what happened and ask for more time.

8. How do you think Maggie's mom will react when she finds out about this problem?

    a. She will understand that Maggie would rather be with her friends than do homework.

    b. She will be disappointed that Maggie lied to her.

    c. She will write the report for Maggie.

Asking Questions

Ask me a question about Antarctica.

Writing Prompt ••

Pretend you are Maggie. How would you apologize to your team for not doing your part of the assignment?

Char likes to help in the kitchen. Her mom is a chef. Char wants to be a cook, too. Char's mom works in a huge hotel. She runs the kitchen at the hotel. She shows Char how to cook new things. They like to work together. They love making pasta.

Characters and Actions 1, *continued*

Main Idea/Details

1. What is the main idea of this story?
   a. Char and her mom like to cook.
   b. Char wants to be a chef.

2. What food do Char and her mom like to cook together?
   a. Dessert
   b. Eggs
   c. Pasta

3. Where does Char's mom work?
   a. A huge hotel
   b. A small restaurant
   c. A big cafeteria

Characters and Actions

4. What does Char like to do?
   a. Help in the kitchen
   b. Watch her mom exercise
   c. Stay at a huge hotel

5. Think about where Char's mom works. What is one word that describes her?
   a. Unskilled
   b. Responsible
   c. Lazy

6. How does Char's mom feel about helping Char in the kitchen?

    a. She thinks Char should do things on her own.

    b. She makes pasta with Char.

    c. She likes showing Char how to do things.

7. What are two reasons Char wants to be a chef?

    a. She likes to help in the kitchen.

    b. She wants to be a chef like her mom.

    c. She wants to work in a huge hotel.

    d. Both *a* and *c*

    e. Both *a* and *b*

8. Look at the picture. How are Char and her mom working together?

Asking Questions

Ask me a question about cooking.

Writing Prompt ···

What food do you know how to prepare? Tell the steps you take to make it.

Mr. Bean and Wags are out for a walk in the park. Wags doesn't need a leash. She usually stays right by Mr. Bean. As they walk, a squirrel darts out in front of them. Wags sees the squirrel, barks, and takes off.

"Come back here," Mr. Bean says. He can't believe Wags has taken off like this. Wags' tail is wagging and she keeps chasing the squirrel through the park. Mr. Bean is frustrated and doesn't know what to do.

Characters and Actions 2, *continued*

Main Idea and Details

1. What is the main idea of this story?
   a. Wags runs away after a squirrel.
   b. Mr. Bean and Wags go for a walk.

2. Where are Mr. Bean and Wags walking?
   a. At a school
   b. In a park
   c. At a zoo

3. What was Wags chasing?
   a. A squirrel
   b. Mr. Bean
   c. A bird

Characters and Actions

4. Why didn't Mr. Bean use a leash to walk Wags?
   a. No one uses leashes in the park.
   b. She likes to chase squirrels.
   c. She usually stays right by Mr. Bean.

5. What tells you Wags is having fun chasing the squirrel?
   a. Her tail is wagging.
   b. She doesn't come back to Mr. Bean.
   c. The squirrel keeps running.
   d. Both *a* and *b*

Characters and Actions 2, *continued*

6. What does Mr. Bean say to Wags?

    a. "Catch that squirrel."

    b. "Don't run away."

    c. "Come back here."

7. Which word doesn't describe how Mr. Bean feels at the end of the story?

    a. Surprised

    b. Amused

    c. Frustrated

8. How do you think the squirrel feels about being chased?

Asking Questions

Ask me a question about Wags and the squirrel.

Writing Prompt ···

Pretend Mr. Bean can't get Wags to come back to him. What do you think Mr. Bean will do next?

"Wow, this is great!" Khan yells. He loves roller coasters. His friend Kent does not like them. He wants to get off. His stomach feels very strange. Kent is sorry Khan talked him into riding along. Kent hopes the ride gets over soon. He wants to ride something else. He will be happy to get his feet back on the ground.

Characters and Actions 3, *continued*

Main Idea and Details

1. What is the main idea of this story?

   a. Riding a roller coaster

   b. Khan and Kent at an amusement park

2. How does the roller coaster make Kent's stomach feel?

   a. Full

   b. Strange

   c. Empty

3. What are the names of the boys in this story?

   a. Kent and Karl

   b. Khan and Ken

   c. Khan and Kent

Characters and Actions

4. Why is Kent riding the roller coaster?

   a. He likes to ride roller coasters.

   b. His friend Khan talked him into riding.

   c. He had a free ticket.

5. What will make Kent happy?

   a. Riding the roller coaster again

   b. Yelling at Khan

   c. Getting his feet back on the ground

Characters and Actions 3, *continued*

6. Find Kent in the picture. Which word does not describe him?

   a. Unhappy

   b. Brave

   c. Frightened

7. What does Khan say that tells you he loves riding roller coasters?

   a. "Wow, this is great!"

   b. "Hey! Stop this thing!"

   c. "Don't you love this, Kent?"

8. Do you think Kent will ever ride a roller coaster again? Explain your answer.

Asking Questions

Ask me a question about roller coasters.

Writing Prompt ••

What's your favorite ride at an amusement park? What's your least favorite ride? Explain your answers.

Jake and Mike are brothers. Mike turns five today. Jake wants to surprise Mike. They will have a party. Jake hangs a sign. Jake's dad bakes a cake. His mom makes pizza. Mike loves pizza. Jake bought Mike a gift. It is a new book.

Mike is next door. He is playing with a friend. He will be back soon. Mike will open the door. Everyone will yell, "Surprise!" They will have fun.

Characters and Actions 4, continued

Main Idea and Details

1. What is the main idea of this story?

    a. Jake and his family are throwing a surprise party.

    b. Mike turns five years old today.

2. What is Jake's dad doing for the party?

    a. Hanging a banner

    b. Baking a cake

    c. Making pizza

3. How old is Mike today?

    a. Ten

    b. Three

    c. Five

Characters and Actions

4. What word does not describe Jake in this story?

    a. Friendly

    b. Helpful

    c. Selfish

5. Why is Mike playing at a friend's house?

    a. His family is getting ready for the surprise party.

    b. He had a fight with his brother.

    c. It is his birthday.

6. What is the best reason that Jake wants Mike's birthday to be special?

   a. Mike loves cake and pizza.

   b. They are brothers.

   c. They are friends.

7. How do we know that people like Mike?

   a. His family wants his birthday to be special.

   b. He is five years old today.

   c. His mom is making him pizza.

8. Do most people like surprise parties? Explain your answer.

Asking Questions

Ask me a question about what Jake is doing in the picture.

Writing Prompt •

Pretend you are Mike. Write a thank-you note to Jake for the surprise party.

Characters and Actions 5 ··················

"I don't think I can do that," the pizza guy says. "You have to pay for the whole thing or I can't leave it."

"But my mom will bring the money to you at your restaurant when she gets home," says Keenan.

"Besides, it's only two dollars and I can't help it if she forgot to leave me enough money."

"Sorry, kid," says the pizza guy. "You can get the pizza when she delivers the money to the restaurant."

"There might be a big tip in it for you," says Keenan.

"What do you mean?" the pizza guy asks.

"If I tell my mom what a nice guy you were, she might give you a big tip when she brings the money," says Keenan.

The pizza guy thinks for a minute and smiles at Keenan. Then he says, "Enjoy your pizza, kid."

Characters and Actions 5, *continued*

Main Idea and Details

1. Which is the best title for this story?
   a. The Pizza That Turned Cold
   b. Keenan's Empty Pockets
   c. Keenan and the Pizza Guy Make a Deal

2. How much more money did Keenan need to pay for the pizza?
   a. One dollar
   b. Two dollars
   c. Four dollars

3. What is the pizza guy's name?
   a. The story doesn't say.
   b. Keenan
   c. Kevin

Characters and Actions

4. Why didn't Keenan have enough money to pay for the pizza?
   a. His mom didn't leave him enough money.
   b. He gave some of the money to a friend.
   c. He couldn't find all the money his mom left.

5. Which word would describe Keenan in this situation?
   a. Clever
   b. Confused
   c. Sorry

6. Whose fault is it that Keenan doesn't have enough money?

    a. The pizza guy's

    b. Keenan's

    c. Keenan's mom

7. Why did the pizza guy let Keenan have the pizza?

    a. He felt sorry for Keenan.

    b. He wanted to get a big tip.

    c. He didn't want the pizza to get cold.

8. Do you think Keenan's mom will be happy with the way he handled the situation? Explain your answer.

Asking Questions

Ask me a question about delivering pizzas.

> **Writing Prompt** •
>
> Pretend you are ordering a pizza over the phone. What exactly would you say?

Trung hopes no one finds him. He is playing hide-and-seek with his cousins.
He thinks he has found the perfect hiding spot. He can hear the other players
moving around in the living room. He's sure no one has found a better spot
than this one. He knows that if he is the last person to be found, he will get to
be "it" next.

Trung hears the kitchen door squeak open. He crouches down under the
table. He closes his eyes. He hears footsteps moving toward the table. Then
they stop. Then he hears, "I see you under there, Trung."

Characters and Actions 6, *continued*

Main Idea and Details

1. What is the main idea of this story?

   a. Trung and his cousins play hide-and-seek.

   b. Trung thinks he has the perfect hiding spot.

   c. Someone finds Trung under the table.

2. What room is Trung hiding in?

   a. The bathroom

   b. The living room

   c. The kitchen

3. In what room does Trung hear other players moving around?

   a. The bathroom

   b. The living room

   c. The kitchen

Characters and Actions

4. Why does Trung want to be the last one found?

   a. So he can join the other players

   b. So he can find a new place to hide

   c. So he can be "it" next

5. What two things help Trung realize someone else is in the room?

   a. The kitchen door squeaks open.

   b. He hears people in the living room.

   c. He hears footsteps.

   d. Both *a* and *c*

   e. Both *a* and *b*

6. How might Trung feel as he thinks he is going to be found?

    a. Lonely

    b. Sad

    c. Angry

7. How does Trung know he has been caught?

    a. Someone taps him on the shoulder.

    b. Someone yells at him from the other room.

    c. Someone says, "I see you."

8. Why do you think Trung closes his eyes when he is under the table?

Asking Questions

Ask me a question about playing hide-and-seek.

> **Writing Prompt** ••
>
> What's your favorite game to play with a group of friends? Tell how
> you play that game.

Carlos and his grandfather got up early. They left for the lake at five o'clock. It was the first time Carlos had ever been fishing. He was excited.

They rowed the boat out onto the lake. Then they dropped their poles in the water. Then they waited. Nothing happened for a long time. As Carlos was about to give up, he felt a tug on his line. His grandfather said, "Just relax and bring it in slowly." The fish jumped out of the water. Carlos kept reeling it in. Carlos could feel his heart beating in his chest as he brought the big fish in.

When they got it in the boat, Carlos' grandfather took his picture with the fish. Then they took it off the hook and put it back in the water.

Main Idea and Details

1. What is the main idea of this story?

    a. Carlos feels his heart beating.

    b. An early morning on the lake

    c. Carlos catches his first fish.

2. Who is Carlos fishing with?

    a. His father

    b. His grandfather

    c. His brother

3. What did they do with the fish?

    a. They let it go.

    b. They took it home.

    c. They lost it.

Characters and Actions

4. Which word does not describe Carlos' grandfather in this story?

    a. Calm

    b. Helpful

    c. Shocked

5. Which word best describes how Carlos felt when he caught the fish?

    a. Frightened

    b. Excited

    c. Disappointed

Characters and Actions 7, *continued*

6. What did the fish do as Carlos was reeling him in?

    a. It jumped out of the water.

    b. It broke the line and got away.

    c. It got stuck in the weeds.

7. Why did Carlos' grandfather take a picture?

    a. In case Carlos never catches another fish

    b. Because the fish would die soon

    c. To celebrate the event

8. Why do you think Carlos and his grandfather let the fish go?

Asking Questions

Ask me a question about fishing.

Writing Prompt •

Think about the first time you did something important (riding your
bicycle, first day of school, etc.). Tell how you felt while you were
doing that.

This lot is next to the community center. It is filled with trash. It is also covered with weeds. It looks awful. The owner will not clean it. He will let the community center use the area if they clean it. Some people volunteered to help. They are helping today.

Carla and her friends like the center. They go there a lot. They also like to help people. They are helping to clean. Carla is raking leaves. Carla and her friends know the center might start a soccer team. They want to play on the team. They can practice on the clean lot.

Characters and Actions 8, *continued*

Main Idea and Details

1. What is the main idea of this story?
   a. The open lot was filled with trash and weeds.
   b. Carla and her friends volunteer to help clean up.
   c. The volleyball team will practice in the open lot.

2. What is Carla doing to help?
   a. Raking
   b. Picking up trash
   c. Painting

3. What kind of team might the center start?
   a. Volleyball
   b. Baseball
   c. Soccer

Characters and Actions

4. Read or listen to each sentence. Tell whether you agree or disagree with each sentence and why.
   a. Carla is a helpful person.
   b. Carla and her friends do not like to volunteer.
   c. The owner of the lot is generous.

5. Which of these might be a reason the owner doesn't want to clean up his own property? Explain why you chose that reason.
   a. He doesn't have the time to do it.
   b. He doesn't use the property, so he doesn't think it's important to clean it up.
   c. He doesn't care what happens to his property.

6. What are two reasons Carla and her friends might be helping to clean up the lot?

    a. They like helping people.

    b. They want to play soccer in the lot.

    c. They have nothing else to do.

    d. Both *b* and *c*

    e. Both *a* and *b*

7. Which of these things are the kids probably not doing to help clean up?

    a. Raking

    b. Picking up garbage

    c. Fixing a fence

8. Look at the boy in the front of the picture. Describe what he is doing.

Asking Questions

Ask me a question about Carla.

Writing Prompt ···

Tell me about a time when you helped someone out. Why did you help the person?

The bands are playing, the clowns are strutting, and the floats are rolling by. It's too bad Megan can't see any of it. The curb is so crowded with people, and she is so short that she can't even catch a glimpse of the parade. She's been pulling on her dad's hand for the last minute to try to get his attention, but he doesn't even seem to notice her. She gives his hand one more big yank.

Her dad cries, "Megan, what are you doing?" Then he looks down at her sad face. He sees she is almost in tears. "Oh, honey, I'm so sorry you couldn't get my attention. I bet you can't see the parade through all these tall people crowded together, can you? Well, hop up here and I'll give you the best seat in the house!"

Megan's dad pulls her up on his shoulders, and she watches the rest of the parade from high in the air. It is the best parade she has ever seen!

Characters and Actions 9, *continued*

Main Idea and Details

1. Which would be the best title for this story?

   a. Megan Looks Over the Crowd

   b. Megan Has a Sad Day

   c. The Big Parade Passes By

2. What was Megan trying to see?

   a. A concert

   b. A circus

   c. A parade

3. How was Megan trying to get her dad's attention?

   a. Tugging on his shirt

   b. Pulling on his hand

   c. Tapping his shoulder

Characters and Actions

4. How did Megan's dad know she was sad?

   a. She was almost in tears.

   b. She told him she was sad.

   c. She was pulling on his hand.

5. How did Megan's dad help her see the parade?

   a. He asked people to move out of the way.

   b. He put her on his shoulders.

   c. He moved her to the front of the crowd.

Characters and Actions 9, *continued*

6. Why was Megan pulling on her dad's hand?

   a. She was bored.

   b. She wanted to hurt him.

   c. She wanted his attention.

7. Which word describes how Megan's dad felt when he looked at her?

   a. Excited

   b. Sorry

   c. Confused

8. Compare how Megan felt at the beginning of the story to how she felt at the end of the story. Why did her feelings change?

Asking Questions

Ask me a question about a parade.

Writing Prompt ••

Pretend you are planning a parade. List five things you would want to see in it.

The Tans are returning from vacation. They have a problem. Their plane arrived an hour ago, but they still can't find their bags.

"There it is," says David, pointing at a suitcase on the conveyer belt. Dad checks the suitcase and shakes his head no.

Anne is getting bored and wants to go home immediately. Mom is trying to keep her quiet, saying, "Just relax, Anne, we can't go home until we have found our luggage."

"What will we do if our bags don't show up, Dad?" David asks.

"We'll have to talk to the airline and see if they can locate our luggage somewhere," Dad says. "Actually, I think that's what we should do right now. Come on, everyone, we're all tired and we need to get home. We'll let the airline worry about delivering our luggage to us."

Characters and Actions 10, *continued*

Main Idea and Details

1. What is the main idea of this story?

    a. The Tans return from vacation.

    b. David Tan spots a suitcase.

    c. The Tans can't find their luggage.

2. How long have the Tans been waiting for their luggage?

    a. A half hour

    b. One hour

    c. Two hours

3. Where are the Tans?

    a. In an airport

    b. On vacation

    c. At home

Characters and Actions

4. What problem do the Tans have?

    a. Anne is bored.

    b. Mr. Tan is ready to go home.

    c. They can't find their luggage.

5. Which two people are looking for the bags?

    a. Anne and Mrs. Tan

    b. Mr. Tan and David

    c. Mr. and Mrs. Tan

6. What is the matter with Anne?

   a. She is bored and wants to go home.

   b. She is mad because she can't find her suitcase.

   c. She is upset because Mom is holding her hand.

7. Which word best describes how everyone is feeling?

   a. Angry

   b. Tired

   c. Calm

8. Do you agree with this statement? **Mr. Tan is very angry about not finding his bags.** Explain your answer.

Asking Questions

Ask me a question about traveling on an airplane.

Writing Prompt ••

Pretend you are Mrs. Tan. What would you do to try to keep Anne quiet as they wait?

Figurative Language 1 ·······················

Ryan and Diane like recess best. They play tag, hopscotch, and dodge ball. They play on the jungle gym. They run races and do gymnastics with their friends. When they go indoors, though, they have a hard time doing their work. Their teacher says, "Stop **clowning around**, you two!"

Ryan and Diane feel ashamed. They stop clowning around. They try to concentrate, but nothing works. They get the giggles and so do the rest of their classmates. Has that ever happened to you?

Figurative Language 1, *continued*

Main Idea and Details

1. What would be a good title for this story?
   a. Kids Have Fun
   b. Clowning Around
   c. My Teacher Gets Mad

2. What does **clowning around** mean?
   a. Acting silly
   b. Acting angry
   c. Dressing in a costume

3. Which one of these do Ryan and Diane like best?
   a. School
   b. Math
   c. Recess

4. Circle **true** or **false**. Ryan and Diane like to play tag.   **true**   **false**

5. What else do they like to play?
   a. Dodge ball and baseball
   b. Hopscotch and dodge ball
   c. Baseball and hopscotch

6. Circle **true** or **false**. After recess, the kids get right back to work.   **true**   **false**

Making Inferences

7. Why do Ryan and Diane have a hard time doing their work after recess?
   a. They like to eat lunch.
   b. They like to play.
   c. They want to go home.

Figurative Language 1, *continued*

8. How does their teacher get Ryan and Diane ready to do their work?

    a. He tells them to clown around.

    b. He punishes them.

    c. He tells them to calm down.

Vocabulary and Semantics

9. What does **get the giggles** mean?

    a. Get sick

    b. Keep laughing

    c. Fooling around

10. What is another name for **recess**?

    a. Play time

    b. Work time

    c. Study time

Figurative Language

11. In this story, what does **clowning around** mean?

Asking Questions

Ask me a question about the teacher.

Writing Prompt •

Write how you would feel about being told to stop clowning around.

Harvey was **sick with worry**. His champion Australian Sheepdog, Lady, was lost. She had been lost for three days. He looked all over the neighborhood. He looked in her house. He looked around the block. He looked at the Humane Society shelter. Where was Lady?

Then Harvey heard a knock at the door. It was the county Pet Patrol. They had Lady! She was dirty and exhausted, but she was fine. The Pet Patrol found Lady at the junkyard. Harvey took Lady. He thanked the officer. He fed Lady and bathed her. They played catch. They went to bed happy.

Figurative Language 2, *continued*

Main Idea and Details

1. Which is the best title for this story?

   a. Pet Patrol to the Rescue!

   b. A Boy and His Dog

   c. Lady! Where Are You?

   d. All of the above

2. Where did Harvey look for Lady?

   a. In the junkyard

   b. In her doghouse

   c. At the vet's office

3. Who found Lady?

   a. Harvey's Dad

   b. The vet

   c. The Pet Patrol

4. How did Lady look when she came home?

   a. Cold and thin

   b. Dirty and tired

   c. Bathed and fed

Narrative Structure

5. What happened in the beginning of the story?

   a. Lady was lost.

   b. Harvey was lost.

   c. Lady was found.

6. What happened in the middle of the story?

    a. Harvey heard a knock at the door.

    b. The Pet Patrol called Harvey.

    c. The Pet Patrol called Harvey's parents.

7. What happened at the end of the story?

    a. Lady ran away.

    b. Lady came home by herself.

    c. Harvey fed and bathed Lady and played catch with her.

Figurative Language

8. In this story, what does **sick with worry** mean?

Asking Questions

Ask me about how Harvey feels about Lady.

Writing Prompt ·····································

In one sentence, write how you would feel if you lost a pet.

"Mom! It's too noisy in here. **I can't hear myself think!**" cried Dan.

"I am not being noisy, Mom," June said.

June and Dan were not getting along. June was singing loudly. Dan was trying to study. Mom said, "You two need to get along."

June put on her earphones. She stopped singing. Dan studied. Later they apologized to each other. They shook hands. It is better to be friends than enemies.

Figurative Language 3, *continued*

Main Idea and Details

1. What is the main idea of this story?

    a. It's good to get along.

    b. Get your sister in trouble.

    c. Listen to Mom.

2. Where was the argument?

    a. At school

    b. In the library

    c. At home

3. What did Dan want to do?

    a. Play

    b. Study

    c. Listen to music

Compare and Contrast

4. How are June and Dan the same?

    a. They both have freckles.

    b. They're in the same family.

    c. They both like music.

5. How are June and Dan different?

    a. Dan is quiet and June is noisy.

    b. Dan likes Coke and June likes milk.

    c. Dan is blond and June has red hair.

Figurative Language 3, *continued*

Defining and Context Clues

6. How do you know Dan and June are brother and sister?

    a. Both kids called the mother Mom.

    b. Both have their own rooms.

    c. Both look alike.

7. How do you know Dan and June made up?

    a. They hugged.

    b. They apologized.

    c. They shook hands.

    d. Both *b* and *c*

Vocabulary and Semantics

8. What does **getting along** mean?

    a. Running fast

    b. Being nice to each other

    c. Moving around

Figurative Language

9. In this story, what does **I can't hear myself think** mean?

Asking Questions

Ask a question about how Dan and June get along.

Ask a question about how their mom helps them get along.

Writing Prompt •

Write something about how you get along with someone.

Greg's Aunt Mary is **as old as a dinosaur**. She's funny, though, and Greg loves being with her. She's all skin and bones. She walks to town with a funny hat on. Greg goes with her. He wears a funny hat, too.

They stop at the ice cream parlor for their favorite cones. They bite off the ends of their cones. They suck the ice cream from the bottoms. Then they stop at the post office. They look at photos of people wanted by the FBI. They frighten each other by making up stories about the offenders.

When they get home, they make hot dogs. They load their franks with mustard. They wrap them in buns and see who can finish faster. They burp and burp. Greg and Aunt Mary wonder what fun stuff they'll do tomorrow.

Figurative Language 4, *continued*

Main Idea and Details

1. What is the main idea of this story?

   a. Aunt Mary likes hats.

   b. Greg and Aunt Mary like to have fun together.

   c. The FBI wants criminals.

2. What did Greg and Aunt Mary like to wear?

   a. Skates

   b. Hats

   c. Mittens

3. What did they stop to eat?

   a. Ice cream cones

   b. Hot dogs

   c. PBJ sandwiches

4. What happened after they ate the hot dogs?

   a. They threw up.

   b. They went to bed.

   c. They burped and burped.

5. What did they look for at the post office?

   a. FBI wanted photos

   b. The postmaster

   c. The new stamps

Figurative Language 4, *continued*

Characters and Actions

6. What does Greg like about Aunt Mary?

   a. She's old.

   b. She's funny.

   c. She's bony.

7. What does Aunt Mary like about Greg?

   a. He likes ice cream.

   b. He likes hot dogs.

   c. He likes to be with her.

Figurative Language

8. In this story, what does **as old as a dinosaur** mean?

Asking Questions

Ask me a question about what they saw in the post office.

Ask me a question about Aunt Mary.

> ### Writing Prompt ....
>
> Write a letter to Greg telling him about your aunt.

Tyne loves to run. She runs each morning. She jumps out of bed and puts on her running clothes and shoes. Then she stretches her legs, back, and arms. Then she runs downstairs, gets a big drink of orange juice, and heads out the back door.

Tyne's favorite place to run is the bike path. She sees friends who are running, too. They run at the same pace till they head for home. In the past, Tyne felt **as limp as a wet rag** as she went home.

The track coach at Tyne's school, Northshore Academy, wanted to get her on the track team. Tyne said she couldn't join because she had to work after school. Coach Rey talked to Tyne's mom. They worked out an agreement. If Tyne would come practice after work, Coach would come back to school and help her.

During practice, Tyne built up her strength. She no longer felt like a limp, wet rag after she ran. Tyne ended that season with three first-place ribbons.

Figurative Language 5, *continued*

Main Idea and Details

1. Which is the best title for this story?
    a. Tyne Runs for It
    b. Tyne and Her Coach
    c. Tyne: A Hard Worker and Talented Runner

2. Where does Tyne like to run?
    a. In the street
    b. On the bike path
    c. On the track

3. Who does Tyne run with?
    a. Her friends
    b. Her mom
    c. Her coach

4. When does Tyne like to run?
    a. After dinner
    b. Before lunch
    c. In the morning

5. What did the coach offer to do for Tyne?
    a. Drive her to school
    b. Come back after work to help her practice
    c. Help her study math

Figurative Language 5, *continued*

Paraphrasing and Summarizing

6. Which is the best way to retell how Tyne gets ready each morning to run?

   a. She gets out of bed, dresses, and runs down the stairs.

   b. She gets out of bed, dresses, and puts on her shoes.

   c. She gets out of bed, dresses, runs down the stairs, and grabs a glass of OJ.

7. Which is the best way to retell how the coach offered to help Tyne?

   a. He said he'd come back after Tyne got off work to coach her.

   b. He said he'd come after school to help Tyne.

   c. He said he'd come before school in the morning to help Tyne.

Figurative Language

8. In this story, what does **as limp as a wet rag** mean?

Asking Questions

Ask me a question about Tyne's mother.

Ask me a question about what Tyne likes to do.

> **Writing Prompt** ••
>
> Write what might have happened if Tyne's coach hadn't offered to help her.

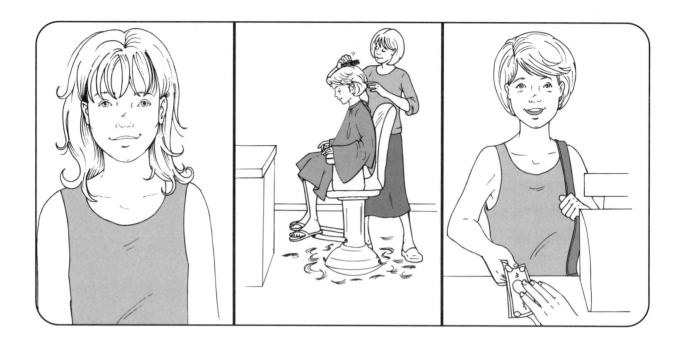

Sal had beautiful, long hair. All of her friends had long hair, too. They loved to curl it, braid it, and streak it. Last night they had a sleepover. They brought all the equipment for their hair, nail polish, and perfume. They spent the night watching movies and making each other look gorgeous.

Today Sal's little brother put bubblegum in her hair. It was a sticky mess! Sal's mom tried to get it out with wax remover. She also tried turpentine and nail polish remover. Nothing took it out. Sal's mom said, "We need to get your hair cut to get the gum out."

Sal went to get her hair cut. She met the stylist, had her hair washed, and closed her eyes. The next time she looked up, the stylist was finishing. Wow! She looked great!

Sal said thanks to the stylist and paid her a tip. Then she paid the cashier. The cashier looked at Sal and said, "**You look prettier than a picture**, Sal."

"Why, thank you. I think I like it, too!" said Sal. She secretly thanked her little brother for his sticky joke!

Figurative Language 6

Main Idea and Details

1. Which is the best title for this story?

   a. Sal's Little Brother

   b. Sal and the Barber

   c. Sal Snips the Sticky Stuff

2. How did Sal and all her friends wear their hair?

   a. Long

   b. Short

   c. In a mohawk

3. Who got bubblegum in Sal's hair?

   a. Her nephew

   b. Her son

   c. Her brother

Sequencing

4. What happened first in this story?

   a. Sal got bubblegum in her hair.

   b. Sal and her friends had a sleepover.

   c. Sal got mad.

5. What happened in the middle of the story?

   a. Sal's brother got bubblegum in her hair.

   b. Sal streaked her hair.

   c. Sal mohawked her hair.

6. What happened at the end of the story?

   a. Sal had her hair cut and hated it.

   b. Sal left the bubblegum in her hair.

   c. Sal had a haircut and loved the new style.

Figurative Language

7. In this story, what does **you look prettier than a picture** mean?

Asking Questions

Ask me a question about how Sal liked her hair at the end of the story.

Writing Prompt •••

Write about a time when you had your hair cut. Did you like it?

Figurative Language 7 ·

"Gee," thought Fran, "Everyone here seems so snobby." It was her first day in a new school. Being in fourth grade was scary enough. Going to a new school in the middle of the year was terrifying.

Fran sulked as she slumped behind her desk. "I'll never get used to this new class. I might as well give up." For the rest of the day, Fran didn't talk to anyone, not even her teacher, Ms. Hart.

As the end-of-the-day bell rang, Ms. Hart came over to Fran. "What's wrong, Fran?" she asked. Fran's eyes filled with tears. She tried to choke them back, but they spilled onto her cheeks.

Fran sniffed and replied, "No one likes me. No one will talk to me. No one wanted to eat lunch with me. Everybody is snobby."

"Fran, **you can't judge a book by its cover**," Ms. Hart said reassuringly. "Simply give the other students time. Be friendly and ask them questions. Soon they'll welcome you to all their activities."

The next day, Fran was as friendly as she could be. She asked Sue for help with math. She asked Tracy to eat lunch with her. She asked Jake if she could borrow a pencil. Soon everyone in the class was crowding around Fran's desk to find out more about her. This was a great day for Fran. She had new friends and she had gained back her confidence.

Figurative Language 7, continued

Main Idea and Details

1. Which is the best title for this story?
   a. Snobby Students
   b. You Can't Judge a Book by Its Cover
   c. Reading Books

2. How did Fran feel on her first day at the new school?
   a. Happy
   b. Afraid
   c. Angry

3. How did Fran feel at the end of her second day at the new school?
   a. Timid
   b. Happy
   c. Afraid

4. How did Fran know that the kids had accepted her?
   a. They left her alone.
   b. They threw stuff at her.
   c. They crowded around her desk and asked her questions.

5. How did Fran's teacher know something was wrong on the first day?
   a. The other kids told her.
   b. Fran was slumping in her chair and sulking.
   c. The teacher was just guessing.

Figurative Language 7, *continued*

Problem Solving

6. What could Fran have done to make friends with the kids the first day?
   a. Asked the teacher for advice
   b. Asked some kids to eat lunch with her
   c. Smiled and been friendly
   d. All of the above

Drawing Conclusions

7. If you were a student in Ms. Hart's class, what would you have thought about Fran the first day?
   a. She was snobby.
   b. She was shy.
   c. She was friendly.
   d. *a* and *b*, but not *c*

Figurative Language

8. In this story, what does **you can't judge a book by its cover** mean?

Asking Questions

Ask me a question about Ms. Hart.

Pretend you are a new student in school. Ask another student to have lunch with you.

Writing Prompt •

Write a different ending to this story.

Figurative Language 8 ·······················

Connie is an excellent dancer. She has studied dance since she was four. Recently, she applied to the Julliard School of Dance. She was accepted. What an honor!

But Connie has a secret. She likes ballet and modern dance, but she loves ballroom dancing. Since she was a sixth grader, she has watched dance contests. She really wants to study ballroom dancing.

Connie told her aunt about her secret. Her aunt didn't say much at first. She just got a faraway look in her eyes.

"Aunt Kate," Connie cried, "Are you listening to me? Please **don't burst my bubble**!"

Aunt Kate said, "I'm sorry, dear. I was just thinking."

"What were you thinking about?" asked Connie.

"I was thinking about when I was your age. I loved to dance. I loved dancing with a partner. Just like you, I loved ballroom dancing the most. Why don't you go to a school for ballroom dancing?"

Connie said, "I never thought about that. Thanks, I will. And all my bubbles thank you!"

Figurative Language 8, *continued*

Main Idea and Details

1. What is the main idea of this story?
   a. Connie wants to study ballroom dancing.
   b. Connie wants to study ballet.
   c. Connie wants to study modern dance.

2. Where was Connie accepted into dance school?
   a. Austin
   b. Richmond
   c. Julliard

3. How old was Connie when she first started dancing?
   a. 10
   b. 4
   c. 6

4. What do Connie and Aunt Kate have in common?
   a. They both love ballroom dancing.
   b. They both like television.
   c. They have the same mother.

Exclusion

5. Tell me something Connie wouldn't have said to her aunt.
   a. I hate to dance.
   b. I like ballet.
   c. I like modern dance.

Figurative Language 8, *continued*

Sequencing

6. What happened to Connie? Pick the sequence that's in the right order.

   a. She got accepted into Julliard. She started dancing at age four. She discovered she liked ballroom dancing best.

   b. She started dancing at age four. She got accepted into Julliard. She discovered she liked ballroom dancing best.

   c. She started dancing at age four. She discovered she liked ballroom dancing best. She got accepted into Julliard.

Figurative Language

7. In this story, what does **don't burst my bubble** mean?

Asking Questions

Ask me a question about Aunt Kate.

Ask me a question about when Connie started dancing.

Writing Prompt ••

Write a prediction about how Connie will fulfill her dream about becoming a ballroom dancer.

It's time for Speech 101, Ling's worst class at Bell Junior High. He despises this class so much that he has put off taking it until now, his last year in junior high.

Ling has tried taking Speech 101 before. Each time he starts taking the course, he withdraws because of stage fright. He gets so nervous before a speech that he shakes, gets chilled, and can't seem to say a word. He knows what he should do before he speaks, like breathe deeply, relax, or go for a long walk. Nothing seems to help.

Now it's time to **take the plunge**. Ling has no choice. He must do the speeches and try to pass the course.

The assignment for the first speech is My Favorite Hobby. Each student must talk with the speech teacher before presenting his speech. Ling chose his hobby and went to see his teacher.

Mr. Gray knows Ling from all the other times he's taken speech. He asked Ling to sit down and tell him about his topic. Ling told him that he likes to work out and lift weights, but he's not sure he can talk about it. Mr. Gray got an excited look on his face and said, "Ling, this is perfect! You can lift weights while you give your speech. Then, you'll breathe deeply, relax, and put all your energy into lifting instead of getting nervous!"

"That's great!" cried Ling.

That day, Ling gave his speech. He lifted weights and talked about safety and body-building. His class listened and applauded. Mr. Gray gave Ling a *B-* on his speech. Ling was happy AND relieved!

Main Idea and Details

1. Which is the best title for this story?

    a. Speech 102

    b. Favorite Hobbies

    c. Ling Overcomes His Fear

2. What used to happen to Ling before he got up to make a speech?

    a. He shook, got chilled, and couldn't speak.

    b. He threw up.

    c. He started crying.

3. Why did Mr. Gray say lifting weights while speaking would be good for Ling?

    a. Ling would build his muscles.

    b. Ling would put all his energy into lifting instead of getting nervous.

    c. Ling wouldn't throw up.

Problem Solving

4. What could Ling have done instead of withdrawing from speech class?

    a. Talked to the teacher to get advice

    b. Quit school

    c. Hidden under his desk

Comparing and Contrasting

5. Speech and drama are similar school subjects. How are they the same?

    a. Both require being in front of others.

    b. Both require speaking in front of others.

    c. Both require wearing costumes.

    d. Both *a* and *b*

Figurative Language 9, continued

Figurative Language

6. In this story, what does **take the plunge** mean?

Asking Questions

Ask me a question about Ling.

Ask me a question about Mr. Gray.

Writing Prompt ●

Write a letter to Ling. Tell him how you feel about speaking in front of others.

Figurative Language 10 ·····················

"He has me **over a barrel**, Dad," exclaimed Jamal. Jamal had a problem with a gang member at school and he wanted his dad's advice about how to handle it.

That afternoon during lunch, Jamal was eating with his friends. Coolie Kid, a gang member who had been tormenting Jamal for weeks, came over to Jamal's table.

"Hey, man, I have an idea. If you want me to leave you alone, I dare you to steal the principal's car. If you don't, I'll keep on bothering you until you can't take it anymore," threatened Coolie Kidd. He walked away.

Jamal shook with anger. "He can't treat me that way," said Jamal to his friends, picking up his tray and heading for class.

After school Jamal waited anxiously for his dad to get home. Jamal told him the whole story. His dad scratched his chin and looked at Jamal.

"He doesn't have you over a barrel, son," said Dad. "You call Coolie Kidd's bluff by telling him you're not going to steal anybody's car or do anything he dares you to. Tell him you don't care about being bothered by him or anyone else. Then see what he does."

The next day, Jamal told Coolie Kidd everything his dad had told him to say. Coolie Kidd seemed surprised. He walked away shaking his head and muttering to himself, "That Jamal is one brave and stubborn dude. I think I'll pick on someone else."

Figurative Language 10, *continued*

Main Idea and Details

1. What is the main idea of this story?

   a. Don't let others intimidate you.

   b. Jamal is a loser.

   c. Crime pays.

2. What did Jamal's dad mean by **calling Coolie Kidd's bluff**?

   a. Playing Blind Man's Bluff

   b. Calling Coolie Kidd names

   c. Not doing what Coolie Kidd said would stop him from tormenting Jamal

3. How would you know that Coolie Kidd was a gang member without being told?

   a. By his hat

   b. By his name

   c. By his dad's occupation

Drawing Conclusions

4. In the middle of the story, what did you think would happen to Jamal?

   a. He'd get beaten up by Coolie Kidd.

   b. He'd make friends with Coolie Kidd.

   c. He'd invite Coolie Kidd to lunch.

Characters and Actions

5. Why do you think Coolie Kidd picked on Jamal?

   a. Jamal is a redhead.

   b. Jamal likes to eat yogurt for lunch.

   c. Jamal is a nice guy who likes school.

6. What do you think Coolie Kidd looks like?

    a. A teddy bear

    b. A Ken doll

    c. A tough guy

Figurative Language

7. In this story, what does having someone **over a barrel** mean?

    a. Putting someone in a tough spot

    b. Draping someone over a barrel

    c. Giving someone a hard time

    d. Both *a* and *c*

Asking Questions

Ask me a question about Jamal.

Ask me a question about Coolie Kidd.

Ask me a question about how Jamal handled his situation.

Writing Prompt ·····························

Write this story from Coolie Kidd's perspective. Here's a start:

"Man, that Jamal is such a wimp. He likes school and he's nice. I think I'll . . . ."

Today is a special day. This day comes in winter. It is the day we give cards. It is the day we give hugs to people we love. It is the day that we decorate our room with hearts. We also have a party. We eat a heart cake and drink pink punch. Can you guess what day it is?

Main Idea and Details

1. Which is the best title for this story?
   a. Valentine's Day
   b. Christmas
   c. My Birthday

2. What is the most important thing about this day?
   a. We have a party.
   b. We give cards.
   c. It is about love.

3. What do we decorate our room with?
   a. Trees
   b. Hearts
   c. Chicks

Comparing and Contrasting

4. How are Valentine's Day and Halloween the same?
   a. You wear costumes.
   b. You go trick or treating.
   c. They are both holidays.

5. How are Valentine's Day and Thanksgiving different?
   a. One is a winter holiday and one is a fall holiday.
   b. One is festive.
   c. One is about fireworks.

Conclusions and Inferences 1

Describing

6. How does your classroom look on Valentine's Day?

    a. It looks drab.

    b. It is decorated with hearts.

    c. It is decorated with witches.

7. What colors go with Valentine's Day?

    a. Blue and purple

    b. Black and brown

    c. Red and pink

Asking Questions

Ask me a question about Valentine's Day.

Ask me a question about Halloween.

Ask me a question about what students do at school on Valentine's Day.

Writing Prompt •

Make a list of things you would need for Valentine's Day decorations.

Deb is washing out Fido's bowl. Deb says, "Fido, you are a good dog. You like to play. You like to be combed and brushed. You like to take long naps. You like to bark at strangers. I know something else you like to do."

Fido listened. He perked up his ears. He stared at Deb. Deb stared back.

"Yes, Fido, I know something else you like to do. You do it every day."

What does Fido like to do?

Conclusions and Inferences 2, *continued*

Main Idea and Details

1. Which is the best title for this story?
   a. Fido Is Good
   b. What, Fido, What?
   c. Fido Likes to Eat

2. What are some things Fido likes to do?
   a. Play
   b. Take long naps
   c. Bark at strangers
   d. All of the above

3. What did Deb mean when she said, "I know something else you like to do"?
   a. Fido likes to eat.
   b. Fido likes his dog house.
   c. Fido likes to do tricks.

Vocabulary and Semantics

4. What is another word for **play**?
   a. Work
   b. Romp
   c. Study

5. What does it mean to be alert?
   a. Sleep
   b. Rest
   c. Pay attention

Conclusions and Inferences 2, *continued*

Narrative Structure

6. What happened in the beginning of this story?

    a. Deb brushed Fido.

    b. Deb washed Fido's bowl.

    c. Deb gave Fido some dog food.

7. What happened at the end of the story?

    a. Deb talked to Fido about something else he liked to do.

    b. Deb patted Fido's head.

    c. Deb went out to play.

Asking Questions

Ask me a question about Fido.

Ask me a question about Deb.

Writing Prompt •

Make a list of things Fido likes to do. Add one more thing to the list that you think he might like to do.

Conclusions and Inferences 3 ··········

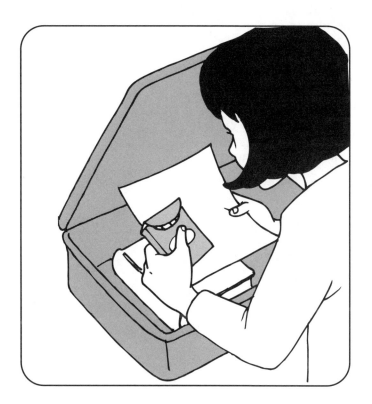

Sue loves school. She is in third grade. She is learning about the Pilgrims.
She knows that they came to this land in 1875. Pilgrims were people from
England who did not want to live there any more. They came across the sea
in ships. They made their homes in the East. They worked hard to farm and
build houses. They liked their freedom.

Today is the day for art. Sue goes to the art room with the rest of her class.
She gets out her crayons and paper. The art teacher says, "You can draw what
you want today, class. It just needs to be about something you are learning in
third grade."

What will Sue draw?

Main Idea and Details

1. Which is the best title for this story?
   a. Pilgrims
   b. Storms at Sea
   c. Sue Loves to Learn

2. What is Sue learning about?
   a. Indians
   b. Thanksgiving
   c. Pilgrims

3. What did the Pilgrims do once they landed on the East coast?
   a. Went swimming
   b. Built farms and houses
   c. Roasted corn

4. After Sue studied the Pilgrims, what class did she go to?
   a. Art
   b. Math
   c. Spelling

Character Attributes

5. What kind of student is Sue?
   a. She likes school.
   b. She doesn't like to learn.
   c. She daydreams a lot.

6. How do you know Sue is a good student?

    a. She loves school.

    b. She loves sports.

    c. She loves her teacher.

Asking Questions

Ask me a question about the Pilgrims.

Ask me a question about what Sue will draw.

Ask me a question about Sue.

Writing Prompt ••

Write something you know about the Pilgrims that wasn't told in this story.

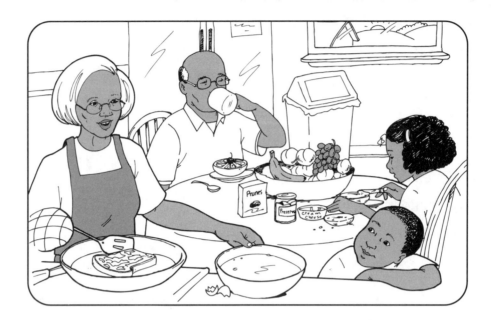

"Time for breakfast!" calls Nana. "Rise and shine! It's French toast, fruit, and bagels. Come and get it!"

It is a beautiful Saturday morning, and Kim and Kevin are spending the weekend with their grandparents. Kim and Kevin love spending time with them and always look forward to time on their farm. There is so much to do! There are horses to ride, fruit to pick, and chickens to feed.

They won't be spending the day on the farm today, though. Nana and Pop are taking them someplace special. The children don't know where. It's a surprise and Nana and Pop won't tell.

Everyone piles in the truck. Kim and Kevin beg for clues about where they are going.

"Well," says Pop, "it's a place where there's a lot to see: animals, produce, concerts, and a rodeo."

"It's a place where there's a lot to eat, too," adds Nana.

"And it's a place where there are contests going on all the time," says Pop.

"Oh, dear," wails Kevin. "I can't guess."

"I can!" cheers Kim. Where are they going?

Conclusions and Inferences 4, _continued_

Main Idea and Details

1. Which is the best title for this story?

   a. Going to the State Fair

   b. A Fun Surprise

   c. Going Places

   d. All of the above

2. What were three things the family was having for breakfast?

   a. Cereal, jam, and toast

   b. Eggs, bacon, and ham

   c. French toast, fruit, and bagels

3. What were the clues Nana and Pop gave the children about where they were going?

   a. A place where they play games, get prizes, and eat cotton candy

   b. A place where there are animals, concerts, and a rodeo

   c. A place where there are animals, lots to eat, and a circus

4. How would they travel?

   a. By truck

   b. By car

   c. By van

Making Inferences

5. Look at the picture. What do you see that tells you it's morning?

   a. Breakfast food and a rooster

   b. Lunch food and kids in their pajamas

   c. Breakfast food and a sunrise

6. Look at the picture again. How do you know the adults are the children's grandparents?

   a. They drink coffee.

   b. They look older than parents.

   c. They're eating prunes.

Asking Questions

Ask me a question about what Nana is cooking.

Ask me a question about what Pop has in his cup.

Ask me a question about the ages of Kim and Kevin.

Writing Prompt •

Make a list of things you would see in a mall. Then write a different middle for the story.

"I need a cool drink on a hot day," said Gay.

"Okay," Lynn said, "but I'm trying not to eat too much junk food that's too high in calories."

Gay got ice cream from the freezer and some fudge sauce from the drawer. Lynn got the milk, ice, and chocolate chips. They put it all in the blender. Gay pressed the *whip* button on the blender and they watched until it was done.

What concoction do you think they made?

Conclusions and Inferences 5, *continued*

Main Idea and Details

1. Which is the best title for this story?
    a. A Chocolate Milk Shake
    b. A Hot Fudge Sundae
    c. The Blender Strikes Back

2. What kind of sauce did they use?
    a. Caramel
    b. Banana
    c. Fudge

3. What kind of day was it?
    a. Cool
    b. Hot
    c. Windy

4. What else did the girls add to the blender that made the shakes chocolaty?
    a. Chocolate milk
    b. Chocolate chips
    c. Bananas

Making Inferences

5. Why didn't Lynn want to eat junk food with lots of calories?
    a. She is a vegetarian.
    b. She is watching her weight.
    c. She is allergic to junk food.

Conclusions and Inferences 5, *continued*

6. Look at the picture. How might you have guessed what the girls were making before you read the story?

   a. By the blender

   b. By the ice cream

   c. Both of the above

Vocabulary and Semantics

7. What is another word for **whip**?

   a. Cut

   b. Chop

   c. Beat

8. Which definition tells about the food with **high calories**?

   a. Food that is high in vitamins

   b. Food that is high in minerals

   c. Food that is high in fat and sugar

Asking Questions

Ask me a question about what kind of milk shake I like.

Ask me a question about what Gay likes to do on a hot day.

> **Writing Prompt** •
>
> Write a recipe for your favorite milk shake. Use just four steps.

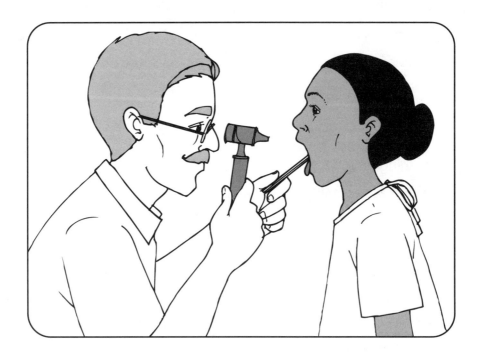

Liz doesn't feel well. She's feverish and she had chills all night. Her throat is sore, too.

"I think you'll have to forget about going to school today, Liz," says her mother. "I'll make an appointment with Doctor Reyes and we'll see if we can get you feeling better soon."

That afternoon, Liz and her mother go to see Doctor Reyes. Liz undresses, puts on a gown, and sits on the examining table. Doctor Reyes comes in to the examining room. He looks in her ears. They are infected. He looks at her throat. Her tonsils are inflamed. He looks in her nose. It looks irritated. He listens to her chest and everything sounds clear.

"You can get dressed now, Liz," the doctor says gently. "You have tonsillitis again, so I need to talk to you and your mom."

After Liz gets dressed, they go to Doctor Reyes' office. He says, "I have a little bit of bad news for you, Liz."

Liz wonders what it will be.

What do you think the bit of bad news is?

Conclusions and Inferences 6, *continued*

Main Idea and Details

1. Which is the best title for this story?

   a. Liz Sees the Doctor

   b. Doctor Reyes

   c. Liz Has Tonsillitis

2. What are two things the doctor did to check Liz's health?

   a. Checked her ears and throat

   b. Checked her reflexes and lungs

   c. Checked her temperature and blood pressure

3. What did Liz wear while the doctor was examining her?

   a. A gown

   b. A warm-up suit

   c. Pajamas

4. What did the doctor say after examining Liz?

   a. "I have some great news."

   b. "I have a little bit of bad news."

   c. "I have a story to tell you."

Defining and Context Clues

5. Which word means the same as **red and swollen**?

   a. Inflamed

   b. Broken

   c. Sprained

6. Which word means **a certain time to be somewhere**?

   a. Noon

   b. Morning

   c. Appointment

7. What does **feverish** mean?

   a. Cold

   b. Having a temperature of over 98.6 degrees

   c. Warm

Asking Questions

Ask me a question about Liz. Start with the word **who**.

Ask me a question about the doctor. Start with the word **what**.

Writing Prompt •••

Rewrite or paraphrase what the doctor told Liz after his examination.

Conclusions and Inferences 7 ············

It's Fair Day at the Boys and Girls' Club and there's so much to do. Every member of the club is there with brothers, sisters, mothers, and fathers. Some children even brought along their grandparents, aunts, and uncles.

Roy and Phil are two friends who came to the fair together. They played in the basketball challenge, competed in the technology twosome, and now they're starting the jalapeno-eating contest.

"Ugh!" burped Roy. "I've only eaten three peppers and I have seven more to go. I'm not sure I'm going to make it."

"I know what you mean," gasped Phil. "I love hot peppers, but I never thought I'd have to eat eight to win this contest."

"The prize is worth the pain, though," said Roy. "I really want that minibike."

"I know. I want it, too, but I don't know if I want it badly enough to set my mouth on fire with these peppers . . . to say nothing of my stomach!"

The boys kept eating and burping. Roy ate two more, which made his total five so far. Phil ate three more, which made his total six. Neither boy wanted to quit, so they kept going.

Finally both boys shoved their chairs away from the table.

"That's it," cried Phil. "I'm done."

"Me, too," gulped Roy.

Which boy do you think won the jalapeno-eating contest? Why?

Main Idea and Details

1. A good name for this story is:

   a. The Peppers Win

   b. Jalapenos 'R Us

   c. The Race to a Spicy Finish

2. What games did Roy and Phil play before the jalapeno-eating contest?

   a. Bingo and hopscotch

   b. Basketball challenge and technology twosome

   c. Basketball and volleyball

3. What relatives did some children bring to the fair?

   a. Aunts and uncles

   b. Brothers and sisters

   c. Grandparents

   d. All of the above

Exclusion

4. What is something Roy wouldn't say about the jalapeno-eating contest?

   a. "These weren't hot at all."

   b. "I love jalapenos."

   c. "Jalapenos are really spicy."

5. What is something the winner wouldn't win after the contest?

   a. A bushel of jalapenos

   b. A minibike

   c. Both of the above

Conclusions and Inferences 7, *continued*

Defining and Context Clues

6. What does the word **challenge** mean in this story?

   a. An invitation to a contest

   b. An invitation to a birthday party

   c. An invitation to the club

7. What is an example of **technology**?

   a. Basketball hoop

   b. Manual scoreboard

   c. Personal computer

Asking Questions

Ask me a question about the Boys and Girls' Club. Start with the word **what**.

Ask me a question about the jalapeno-eating contest. Start with the word **why**.

> **Writing Prompt** •••
>
> Make a list of clubs in your school. Then write a short paragraph about which one you like best.

Sam is a paraplegic, which means he has no feeling in his legs. He has good use of his upper body and arms, though, so there isn't much he can't do.

Sam has a bit of a problem, though. He loves to eat and he has grown obese in the past few years. His doctor has warned him about being obese. Sam feels bad, but he's not quite sure what to do. So he asked his doctor.

"Well, there are three things you can do, Sam, to lose weight," said Dr. Dean. "You can get more exercise, limit your intake of fat and sugar, and drink lots of water."

Sam agreed to do all three things. He knew he should drink at least eight glasses of water per day. He also knew he should eat healthy food like fruit, vegetables, chicken, and fish. He was not sure about how to be more active, since he only had use of his upper body. The doctor asked him to go to the health center for help.

Sam went for help. He talked to a fitness expert. He got advice about how to exercise. What do you think the fitness expert told Sam about his exercise?

Main Idea and Details

1. Which is the best title for this story?

    a. Sam Gets Fit

    b. Sam Takes Charge

    c. Sam Is Obese

2. What did the doctor tell Sam about his obesity?

    a. Limit your intake of vitamins.

    b. Eat lots of fat and protein.

    c. Limit your intake of fat and sugar.

3. What did Sam know about healthy eating?

    a. He should eat dessert first.

    b. He should eat fruit and vegetables.

    c. He should drink diet pop.

Character Attributes

4. What did Sam know about his weight?

    a. He was obese.

    b. He was obtuse.

    c. Both of the above

5. How did Sam feel about his obesity?

    a. He was happy.

    b. He was angry.

    c. He felt bad.

Definitions

6. What does **obese** mean?

    a. Overweight

    b. Underweight

    c. Paralyzed

7. What does **paraplegic** mean?

    a. He can use a periscope.

    b. He is paralyzed in two of his limbs.

    c. He is fat.

Asking Questions

Ask me a question about Sam. Start with the word **how**.

Ask me a question about being a paraplegic. Start with the word **why**.

Writing Prompt ···

Write a prescription for Sam about his diet, exercise, and water intake.

"Mom, look, I found a shell!"

"Dad, look, I made a sandcastle!"

Avery and Kevin were having a wonderful day. They had left home early this morning with everything they needed loaded in the trunk of the car. They brought towels, buckets, shovels, hats, and sunglasses. Mom packed a picnic lunch with all their favorite food. Dad put gas in the car the night before so they could get an early start.

"Well, let's see that shell," said Mom. "Wow, it's in perfect shape. Hold it to your ear. Can you hear something?"

"I can!" exclaimed Avery.

"Let's see that sandcastle, Kevin," urged Dad. "Wow, it's really complicated!"

They all played until sunset when Avery and Kevin's parents said it was time to head home. They agreed tiredly and fell asleep in the car.

Where had they been all day?

Conclusions and Inferences 9, continued

Main Idea and Details

1. Which is the best title for this story?
   a. At the Hotel
   b. At the Beach
   c. At Home

2. What two things did Avery and Kevin want to show their parents?
   a. A nest and bird eggs
   b. A hole in the sand and a shell
   c. A shell and a sandcastle

3. How late did they stay at the beach?
   a. Until sunset
   b. Until sunrise
   c. Until dinner

4. What things did they pack in the car that morning?
   a. Food, their dog, and sunglasses
   b. Buckets, shovels, sunglasses, hats, towels, and a picnic
   c. Blankets, buckets, and shovels

Vocabulary and Semantics

5. What is another word for **complicated**?
   a. Easy
   b. Detailed
   c. Wonderful

6. What is another word for **bucket**?
   a. Pail
   b. Shovel
   c. Barrel

Conclusions and Inferences 9, *continued*

Definitions

7. What time of day is sunset?

   a. Morning

   b. Afternoon

   c. As the sun goes down

Inferencing

8. Mom said, "Hold the shell to your ear. Do you hear anything?"

   Avery said, "Yes, I can!"

   What do you think Avery heard?

   a. The ocean

   b. A bird

   c. An orchestra

Asking Questions

Ask me a question about the beach. Start with the word **where**.

Ask me a question about the children. Start with the word **who**.

Writing Prompt ·

Write a paragraph about how you felt the first time you went to the beach. If you've never been to the beach, write about a favorite place you like to visit.

"We love you," sighed Ginger and Michael. "We've been waiting for you a long time and now you're here."

Ginger and Michael are the proud, delighted parents of Jack. He weighed seven pounds and was twenty-two inches long when he was born. He is three months old now and he's sleeping throughout the night. What a miracle he is!

Every day, after Michael goes to work, Ginger dresses Jack in a fleecy parka, warm booties, and corduroy pants. They get out the stroller and take a walk to an apartment building a few blocks away. Once there, they visit a friend who loves Jack as much as his parents do. When Jack gets fussy, he and his mom head home for a bottle and a nap.

When Michael gets home from work, Jack is waiting. He sees his dad and he giggles and coos.

"Well, little fella, what did you do today?" asks Michael. "Did you ride a big horse and lasso a monster?"

Jack giggles and so does his mom. She wonders what they ever did before they got Jack just two weeks ago.

Why didn't Ginger and Michael get Jack until just two weeks ago?

Readability 4.7

Story Comprehension To Go   246

Main Idea and Details

1. Which is the best title for this story?
   a. Michael Goes to Work
   b. Welcome, Jack!
   c. Ginger and Jack Take a Walk

2. What does Jack wear when he goes for a walk in his stroller?
   a. A parka, pants, and booties
   b. A sweatshirt, shorts, and shoes
   c. A sweater, leggings, and socks

3. Who is waiting for Michael when he gets home from work?
   a. Michael
   b. Jack
   c. Both of the above

4. What did Michael ask Jack about his day?
   a. Did you play in the park?
   b. Did you ride a big horse and lasso a monster?
   c. Did you bake a cake with Mom?

Definitions

5. What is the definition of a **parka**?
   a. A nightgown
   b. Slippers
   c. A jacket

6. What does **adoption** mean?

   a. A family gets a baby that was born to someone else.

   b. The baby is born to the family.

   c. The baby comes from the stork.

7. What is **corduroy**?

   a. A type of milk shake

   b. A type of toy

   c. A type of fabric

Asking Questions

Ask me a question about Ginger and Michael. Start with the word **how**.

Ask me a question about Jack. Start with the word **when**.

Writing Prompt •

Write about someone you know who has a baby. Tell about how the baby sleeps, eats, and plays.

Paraphrasing and Summarizing 1 ·······

Today Ann was five years old. She had a birthday party. Her mom baked a special cake. She frosted it with pink icing. She put five candles on the cake.

Ann's guests came to the party. They each brought a present for her. They all played games. Then Ann sat down at the table. She said, "Time for cake and ice cream!"

Next Ann opened her presents. Then she gave each guest a favor. What a great birthday!

Paraphrasing and Summarizing 1, *continued*

Main Idea and Details

1. What is the main idea of this story?

    a. Ann's special cake

    b. Ann's birthday party

    c. Ann's guests

2. How old is Ann?

    a. Five

    b. Six

    c. Seven

3. What did Ann's guests do before they had cake and ice cream?

    a. They put candles on the cake.

    b. They opened Ann's presents.

    c. They played games.

Paraphrasing and Summarizing

4. Which sentence means the same as this sentence?

    The cake was baked by Ann's mom.

    a. Ann's mom frosted the cake.

    b. Ann's mom baked the cake.

    c. Ann baked the cake for her birthday.

5. What did the guests do at the party?

    a. They brought presents, played games, and ate cake and ice cream.

    b. They decorated the cake and gave favors to Ann.

    c. They sang songs, played games, and painted pictures.

6. Which sentence means the same as this sentence?

   Time for cake and ice cream!

   a. It's three o'clock!

   b. Let's eat cake and ice cream!

   c. It takes time to fix cake and ice cream.

7. Which sentence means the same as this sentence?

   After the cake and ice cream, Ann opened her presents.

   a. Ann opened her presents before everyone ate cake and ice cream.

   b. The presents were opened before the cake and ice cream were served.

   c. Before Ann opened presents, cake and ice cream were served.

8. Summarize this story in your own words.

Asking Questions

Ask me a question about Ann's birthday party.

> **Writing Prompt** ··
>
> Pretend you will have a birthday party. Write an invitation for
> someone to come to your party. Tell when and where it will happen.

Paraphrasing and Summarizing 2 ....

Ben makes a great sandwich. First he spreads butter on some bread. Then he adds some lettuce. Next he adds a tomato slice. Then he adds cheese. He puts two pickle slices on top. Then he spreads mustard on a slice of bread. He stacks the slice on top. Then the sandwich is all set to eat!

We love Ben's sandwiches. We take them with us for lunch. They make any picnic perfect!

Paraphrasing and Summarizing 2, *continued*

Main Idea and Details

1. What is the main idea of this story?

   a. Ben's picnics

   b. Ben's sandwiches

   c. Family picnics

2. What does Ben put on after the lettuce?

   a. Two pickle slices

   b. One tomato slice

   c. One onion slice

3. Which things go into Ben's sandwich?

   a. Pickle slices, lettuce, cheese, and jelly

   b. Mustard, tomato, lettuce, and onion

   c. Tomato, cheese, lettuce, and pickle slices

Paraphrasing and Summarizing

4. What does **stacks** mean in this sentence?

   He stacks the bread on top of the sandwich.

   a. Throws

   b. Piles

   c. Smashes

5. Which sentence means the same as this sentence?

   They make any picnic perfect.

   a. Ben's sandwiches would be great for any picnic.

   b. A picnic without Ben's sandwiches is not fun.

   c. You can't have a good picnic without Ben's sandwiches.

6. What does **all set** mean in this sentence?

   Then the sandwich is all set to eat.

   a. Going

   b. Ready

   c. Almost

7. Explain how Ben makes a sandwich. Tell the steps in the order Ben does them.

8. Summarize this story in your own words.

Asking Questions

Ask me a question about how Ben makes a sandwich.

Writing Prompt •

What is your favorite kind of sandwich? Draw a picture of it and write the directions for making your sandwich.

Each year, Mark's town holds a snowman contest. The first prize is a super-slick sled. Last year, Mark won the third prize. He won a free pizza. This year, Mark hoped to win the first prize.

Mark thought about how to build his snowman. This year, he would take his time and make a great snowman. It would be a sled-winner for sure!

Mark found supplies for his snowman. He found a great scarf in the hall closet. He took a hat from an old costume. He gathered dark, round rocks that were different sizes. Next Mark looked for two tree branches for arms. It took a long time to find just the right ones. He trimmed the leaves off the two branches to make matching arms. Then he had to wait for the contest to start.

The day of the contest finally came. First Mark rolled three snowballs. He packed each one to make it round and smooth. Then he rolled the snowballs to make them bigger. He made three sizes. The biggest ball was the bottom of the snowman. The medium-sized ball was the middle. Mark stacked it on top of the big ball.

The top ball was the head. Mark reached high to stick it on. He patted some snow around the snowman's neck. That would keep the head on for sure. Then Mark dressed his snowman. He stuck a fresh, whole carrot in for the nose. Now all he had to do was wait for the judges.

Paraphrasing and Summarizing 3, *continued*

Main Idea and Details

1. What is the main idea of this story?

    a. Mark wins a snowman contest.

    b. Mark makes a snowman for a contest.

    c. Mark collects supplies to make a snowman.

2. What prize did Mark win in last year's snowman contest?

    a. Free movie tickets

    b. A snowboard

    c. A free pizza

3. Where did Mark find a good hat for his snowman?

    a. An old costume

    b. A magic set

    c. In the hall closet

Paraphrasing and Summarizing

4. What does **super-slick sled** mean in this sentence?

    The first prize is a super-slick sled.

    a. A sled that is greasy

    b. A sled that is large and shiny

    c. A sled that goes very fast

5. Which sentence means the same as this sentence?

    His snowman would be a sled-winner for sure!

    a. His snowman would certainly ride a sled in the contest.

    b. His snowman would definitely win the sled as a prize.

    c. His snowman would surely ride on a sled to win the contest.

6. Which sentence tells how Mark gathered his supplies?

    a. Mark found all the things he needed in one place.

    b. Mark took a long time to find all the things he needed for his snowman.

    c. Mark gathered everything he needed in just a few minutes.

7. Which sentence means the same as this sentence?

    Now all he had to do was wait for the judges.

    a. Mark would have to wait a long time for the judges to come.

    b. Mark's snowman was ready for the judges to see.

    c. Mark had to wait for the judges to build their own snowmen.

8. Summarize this story in your own words.

Asking Questions

Ask me a question about this story.

Writing Prompt •••

The first prize for the snowman contest was a super-slick sled. Think of a good second prize for this contest. Describe the prize.

Paraphrasing and Summarizing 4 ·······

Trish came over to Jan's house. She had her sleeping bag and a pillow with her. The girls went right to the backyard. A tent was set up there.

Trish and Jan put their sleeping bags and some pillows in the tent. Then they went inside for dinner. Jan put fresh food in Snowball's bowl, but she could not find her cat. "Where is Snowball?" she wondered.

After dinner the girls took a flashlight to the tent. They got in their sleeping bags. They read stories to each other. Everything was cozy.

Suddenly Jan said, "Yikes! Something is moving in my sleeping bag!"

"What is it?" cried Trish. The girls watched the lump move slowly up the sleeping bag. Their eyes were as big as saucers. The lump would soon be out of the sleeping bag.

"This is freaking me out!" Jan said. "Turn on the flashlight!"

Trish turned the flashlight on. She pointed it at the lump. The lump purred. Snowball crept out of the sleeping bag. She licked Jan's face. "I guess Snowball wants to camp out with us, too!" Jan giggled.

Paraphrasing and Summarizing 4, *continued*

Main Idea and Details

1. What is the main idea of this story?

   a. Snowball camps out.

   b. Two girls get ready to spend the night in a tent.

   c. Trish comes over to visit Jan.

2. What did Trish bring to Jan's house?

   a. A white cat

   b. A flashlight and a book

   c. A sleeping bag and a pillow

3. Where was the tent set up?

   a. In Trish's backyard

   b. In Jan's basement

   c. In Jan's backyard

Paraphrasing and Summarizing

4. Which sentence means the same as this sentence?

   The girls went right to the backyard.

   a. The girls turned right to get to the backyard.

   b. The girls went to the backyard on the right.

   c. The girls went immediately to the backyard.

5. Which sentence means the same as this sentence?

   This is freaking me out!

   a. I'm frightened!

   b. It's strange!

   c. I need to get out!

6. Which sentence means the same as this sentence?

   They took turns reading stories to each other.

   a. They read stories aloud to each other.

   b. They alternated reading stories to each other.

7. Which sentence means the same as this sentence?

   Their eyes were as big as saucers.

   a. They were getting sleepy.

   b. They were very scared.

   c. It was hard for them to see well inside the tent.

8. Summarize this story in your own words.

Asking Questions

Ask me a question about this story.

Writing Prompt •

Imagine that you can sleep overnight in a tent. Write what you will do to have a great time.

Lisa was in a hurry to get home. She wanted to get started on her science project right away. She would plant some seeds. She would see how fast they sprouted. Then she would give each plant different light. She would check how much they grew each day.

Lisa didn't watch where she was walking. Right in front of her house, she tripped. She scraped her knee. It was bleeding. Lisa knew just what to do.

Lisa washed her knee carefully and patted it dry. Then she dabbed some antiseptic cream on the scrape. She was careful not to let the tip of the cream touch her wound. When the cream had dried a bit, she covered the scrape with a bandage.

Lisa put all the first-aid supplies away. Then she was all set to start her science project.

Paraphrasing and Summarizing 5, *continued*

Main Idea and Details

1. What is the main idea of this story?
    a. Lisa's science project
    b. First-aid supplies
    c. Lisa's injury

2. Why didn't Lisa watch where she was walking?
    a. She was thinking about something else.
    b. She couldn't see the sidewalk.
    c. The sun was shining in her eyes.

3. Where did Lisa fall on the sidewalk?
    a. Three blocks from her house
    b. Two blocks from her house
    c. In front of her house

Paraphrasing and Summarizing

4. Which sentence means the same as this sentence?

    Then she would put them under different light conditions.

    a. Then she would give each plant a different kind of light.
    b. Then she would feed each plant a different kind of soil.
    c. Then she would cover each plant with light paper.

5. What does this sentence from the story mean?

    She scraped her knee.

    a. She scratched her knee with her fingernails.
    b. She bruised her knee.
    c. Some of the skin on her knee was rubbed off.

6. Which sentence tells how Lisa took care of her injury?

   a. Lisa asked for help to take care of her scraped knee.

   b. Lisa gave herself first-aid.

   c. Lisa did not know how to take care of her injury.

7. Which sentence means the same as this sentence?

   Then she dabbed some antiseptic cream on the scrape.

   a. Lisa put a small bit of antiseptic cream on the scrape.

   b. Lisa put a lot of antiseptic cream on the scrape.

   c. Lisa poured some antiseptic cream on the scrape.

8. Summarize this story in your own words.

Asking Questions

Ask me a question about this story.

Writing Prompt •••

Write about an injury you had. Tell how it happened and how it got better.

Paraphrasing and Summarizing 6 ·······

Beth loves her dog, Scraps. Even though Scraps is a big dog, he is obedient.

When Scraps was a puppy, he and Beth went to dog training sessions. Each lesson taught a different behavior. The instructor would demonstrate giving a command. Then his dog would follow the command. Next the students tried giving the command for their dogs to obey. Scraps learned quickly. He became a model dog.

Soon Beth could take Scraps for walks without any worries. He didn't pull on the leash or try to run away. He didn't jump up on people or sniff them.

One day Scraps forgot his training. Beth took Scraps to the park for a walk. Things went smoothly for a while. Then Scraps spotted a woman eating ice cream. Scraps was hungry. The ice cream was too tempting for him.

With a mighty jerk, Scraps broke loose from Beth. He grabbed the woman's ice cream cone with his big mouth.

"No, Scraps! Sit!" Beth cried. She grabbed the leash and pulled Scraps away from the woman. Scraps wolfed down the rest of the cone. Then he sat down politely.

"I'm very sorry," Beth said. "Scraps usually behaves much better."

"No harm done," the woman laughed. "I'm trying to diet, anyway. Your dog did me a favor!"

Main Idea and Details

1. What is the main idea of this story?

    a. Scraps makes a mistake

    b. Beth likes ice cream

    c. Scraps learns to sit

2. What kind of training did Beth and Scraps have together?

    a. Training dogs to behave

    b. Training dogs to do tricks

    c. Training dogs to sniff people

3. What made Scraps forget his training?

    a. He wanted to chase a ball.

    b. The noise in the park scared him.

    c. He wanted to eat the ice cream cone.

Paraphrasing and Summarizing

4. Which sentence is the best description of Scraps?

    a. Scraps is a big dog that behaves well most of the time.

    b. Scraps is a big dog that often does not behave well.

    c. Scraps is a big dog that never obeys orders.

5. What does **a model dog** mean in this sentence?

    Scraps learned quickly and became a model dog.

    a. A dog that poses for pictures

    b. A dog that wears clothing

    c. A well-trained dog

6. Which sentence means the same as this sentence?

    Soon Beth could take Scraps for walks without any worries.

    a. Soon Scraps didn't worry on walks anymore.

    b. Soon Scraps behaved well on walks with Beth.

    c. Soon Beth didn't worry that someone would steal Scraps on a walk.

7. Which sentence means the same as this sentence?

    Scraps wolfed down the rest of the cone.

    a. Scraps licked the cone until he finished it.

    b. Scraps sat down on the cone like a wolf.

    c. Scraps ate the whole cone very quickly.

8. Summarize this story in your own words.

Asking Questions

Ask me a question about this story.

Writing Prompt ·

Write about what makes a perfect dog. Tell what the dog looks like and acts like. Tell what is special about the dog. Don't forget to give your dog a name!

Readability 3.2

Story Comprehension To Go

266

Paraphrasing and Summarizing 7 ·······

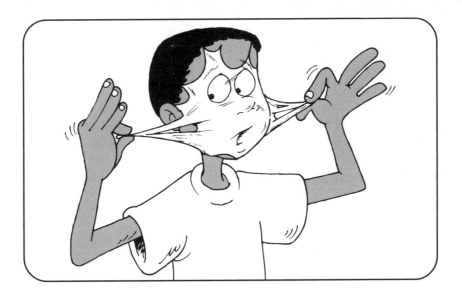

Gregg was mean. He teased kids. He called them names. He laughed at their mistakes. Sometimes he tripped someone just for the fun of it.

One day the teacher said, "Class, let's have a contest. We will see who can blow the biggest gum bubble. We'll measure each one and chart the results. The winner will get ten pieces of gum."

The teacher gave each student a piece of gum. The students chewed their gum for ten minutes. Then they blew their bubbles individually.

Karen's bubble popped before it was even an inch. Gregg sneered, "Great bubble!" Everyone ignored him.

Finally it was Gregg's turn. "Watch this!" he said. He closed his eyes. He blew a small bubble. Slowly it grew bigger. It got so big, it covered up his face. Then pop! It exploded. Gum stuck all over his face.

Gregg opened his sticky eyes. He was sure everyone would laugh at him. After all, he had laughed at them lots of times. But no one did. Karen said, "Try again, Gregg."

Gregg was ashamed. He was sorry he had been so mean. From now on, he would be nice to everyone.

Main Idea and Details

1. Which is the best title for this story?

   a. Gregg's Bubble Pops

   b. Gregg Makes a Mess

   c. Gregg Learns a Lesson

2. What was special about Gregg?

   a. He was short.

   b. He was mean.

   c. He was a champion at blowing bubbles.

3. How big was Karen's bubble?

   a. One inch

   b. Less than one inch

   c. More than one inch

Paraphrasing and Summarizing

4. What does **individually** mean in this sentence?

   Then they blew their bubbles individually.

   a. Two people at a time

   b. All at the same time

   c. One person at a time

5. Which sentence means the same as this sentence?

   Watch this!

   a. You'll be amazed at what happens next.

   b. You won't like what happens next.

   c. What happens next will be boring.

6. Which sentence means the same as this sentence?

   Everyone ignored him.

   a. All the other students teased him.

   b. None of the students teased him.

   c. No one paid any attention to him.

7. What lesson did Gregg learn?

   a. Treat other people the way you want them to treat you.

   b. Don't blow bubblegum bubbles in public.

   c. Teasing other people is fun.

8. Summarize this story in your own words.

Asking Questions

Ask me a question about Gregg.

> **Writing Prompt** ·
>
> The class would make a chart about the bubblegum bubbles. Tell
> what information the chart would include. Draw a sketch of the chart.
> What could the students learn from this lesson?

Everyone had a great time at Camp Tall Tree. The weather was suitable for swimming. Some campers hiked up the mountain trails. Other campers hiked down to the river and back.

Each camper had a daily chore. Some campers cleaned the bathrooms. Others helped to prepare meals. Others chopped wood for fires.

After lunch the campers took a nap. Then they wrote to their families.

One day a park ranger gave a lecture about fires. He showed how to make a safe campfire. He showed how to put a fire out.

At night the campers sat around a big campfire. They sang songs and listened to stories. Then they went to bed. Everyone went right to sleep.

Camp Tall Tree is over for this summer. The campers can't wait till next year!

Paraphrasing and Summarizing 8, *continued*

Main Idea and Details

1. What is the main idea of this story?
   a. Preventing forest fires
   b. Fun around the campfire
   c. Fun at Camp Tall Tree

2. Where did campers hike?
   a. On the mountain and to the lake
   b. To the river and on the mountain
   c. To the pond and the river

3. When will Camp Tall Tree be open again?
   a. Next month
   b. Next week
   c. Next year

Paraphrasing and Summarizing

4. What sentence means the same at this sentence?
   The weather was suitable for swimming.
   a. Everyone wore swimsuits to go swimming.
   b. The weather was good for swimming.
   c. The weather was not good for swimming.

5. Which sentence means the same as this sentence?
   Each camper had a daily chore.
   a. Campers each did a job every day.
   b. Campers all did the same job every week.
   c. Some campers did a job every day.

6. Which sentence means the same as this sentence?

   One day a park ranger gave a lecture about fires.

   a. One day a park ranger scolded the campers about setting fires.

   b. One day a park ranger asked the campers to start fires.

   c. One day a park ranger gave the campers information about fires.

7. Which sentence means the same as this sentence?

   Everyone went right to sleep.

   a. Everyone was asleep very quickly.

   b. Everyone slept on the right side of the bed.

   c. Everyone turned right to go to bed.

8. Summarize this story in your own words.

Asking Questions

Ask me a question about Camp Tall Tree.

Writing Prompt ••

Pretend that you are a camper at Camp Tall Tree. Write a letter to your family.

Today was a memorable day for Ed. He and his dad went to the pet shop as soon as it opened in the morning. Ed had waited a long time to select his first pet.

Ed had thought long and hard about selecting an appropriate pet. He didn't want a pet that required constant care. Ed couldn't be interrupted while he practiced playing his flute. He also needed to concentrate while he did his homework.

Ed wasn't fond of reptiles. They weren't very friendly. He didn't want a large pet because he wanted one that could stay in his room. Ed enjoyed playing with cats and dogs, but he was allergic to them. He liked gerbils and hamsters, but they are nocturnal. They might keep him awake all night.

"How about a parakeet?" Dad asked. "You could keep the cage in your room. You could teach it to talk to you."

"A parakeet would be awesome!" Ed said. His dad helped him choose a birdcage and some toys for his bird. They bought some birdseed, too. Then Ed zeroed in on the ideal parakeet. He chose a green parakeet with yellow markings.

Ed and his dad took the bird and the supplies home. They set up the cage in Ed's room. The parakeet was instantly at home. Ed had finally found his perfect pet!

Paraphrasing and Summarizing 9, *continued*

Main Idea and Details

1. What is the main idea of this story?
   a. Ed goes to a pet store.
   b. Ed's room
   c. Ed chooses a perfect pet.

2. What instrument did Ed play?
   a. Piano
   b. Flute
   c. Violin

3. Why didn't Ed choose a cat or a dog?
   a. He is scared of them.
   b. They are too noisy.
   c. He is allergic to them.

Paraphrasing and Summarizing

4. Which sentence means the same as this sentence?

   Today was a memorable day for Ed.
   a. Ed remembered today's date.
   b. Ed would always remember this day.
   c. Today Ed remembered something important.

5. Which sentence means the same as this sentence?

   Ed had thought long and hard about selecting an appropriate pet.
   a. For a long time, Ed didn't think about getting a pet for himself.
   b. Ed had known for a long time exactly what pet he wanted.
   c. Ed thought carefully about which pet would be a good choice for him.

6. What does **they are nocturnal** mean in this sentence?

   He liked gerbils and hamsters, but they are nocturnal.

   a. They are active at night, not during the day.

   b. They make noises all day and night.

   c. They need to be outside at night.

7. Which sentence means the same as this sentence?

   Then Ed zeroed in on the ideal parakeet.

   a. Then Ed got very close to a perfect parakeet.

   b. Then Ed chose the perfect parakeet.

   c. Then Ed flapped his arms at a perfect parakeet.

8. Summarize this story in your own words.

Asking Questions

Ask me a question about having a parakeet as a pet.

Writing Prompt ••

Think about what a great pet store would look like. What would you see there? What kinds of animals could you buy there? What kinds of cages would you see? Describe a perfect pet store.

Kent City has a new skate park. It has ramps of several different heights and lots of space for skaters. There is a huge curved area perfect for flips and stunts.

Tony was an awesome inline skater. He had won skating contests with his championship jumping. Tony flipped with the best of them. As soon as the skate park opened, Tony spread the word to everyone.

"Let's check out the new skate park this afternoon," he suggested to his friends. "Bring your helmets and kneepads. We're going to have some wild rides!"

Tony's friends were anxious about skating in the park. They all had inline skates, but none of them could skate anywhere near as well as Tony. Jeff and Dan had only had their skates on once before. Kevin knew how to skate on fairly flat ground, but he was nervous about taking any ramps. The boys agreed to give the new park a shot, but only Tony planned to skate like crazy.

As soon as they arrived at the park, Tony sped off to practice his flips. Jeff skated around the park, staying near the fence in case he needed to grab it. Dan couldn't stop himself from skating over a branch, which made him fall on his knees. Since he wasn't wearing kneepads, his knees really hurt. Kevin saw Dan fall. "I'd better watch where I'm skating," Kevin thought. He began to perspire just thinking about it.

Dan stopped skating and watched the others. Kevin and Jeff skated faster and faster. Before long, Kevin tried his skill on the lowest ramp. Whoosh, he landed safely and kept on skating. By the end of the afternoon, Kevin was taking the ramps like a champ.

"Aren't you glad we came to the new park?" asked Tony.

"Without a doubt!" Kevin said. On the way home, the boys planned their next trip to the new skate park.

Paraphrasing and Summarizing 10, continued

Main Idea and Details

1. What is the main idea of this story?

    a. Tony and his friends skate at the new park.

    b. Tony does great stunts at the park.

    c. Watching Tony do skate stunts

2. How do you know Tony is a good inline skater?

    a. He said so.

    b. He skated well at the park.

    c. He has won skating contests.

3. What did Tony tell his friends to wear at the skate park?

    a. Wrist pads and kneepads

    b. Elbow pads and helmets

    c. Helmets and kneepads

Paraphrasing and Summarizing

4. What does **ramps of several different heights** mean in this sentence?

    It has ramps of several different heights and lots of space for skaters.

    a. Several ramps that are all the same size and shape

    b. Several ramps that are not all the same height

    c. Neither *a* or *b*

5. What does **taking any ramps** mean in this sentence?

    Kevin knew how to skate on fairly flat ground, but he was nervous about taking any ramps.

    a. Stealing ramps from the park

    b. Skating up any ramps in the park

    c. Moving ramps in the park

6. Which sentence means the same as this sentence?

   The boys agreed to give the new park a shot.

   a. The boys agreed to shoot squirt guns in the new park.

   b. The boys agreed to take a picture of the new park.

   c. The boys agreed to try skating at the new park.

7. Which sentence means the same as this sentence?

   Tony planned to skate like crazy.

   a. Tony planned to act crazy while he skated.

   b. Tony planned to skate fast and do as many stunts as he could.

   c. Tony planned to skate with his eyes closed.

8. Summarize this story in your own words.

Asking Questions

Ask me a question about this story.

Writing Prompt ••

Write your opinion about inline-skating. Tell why you think it's a good sport or a bad sport.

Answer Key

Some answers are given as sample responses; accept other logical, appropriate answers as correct. No answers have been provided for unnumbered questions because these answers will vary based on students' personal experiences, perspectives, etc.

Vocabulary and Semantics 1
pp. 7-9
1. c
2. d
3. c
4. d
5. b
6. d
7. d

Vocabulary and Semantics 2
pp. 10-12
1. a
2. a
3. c
4. d
5. a
6. a
7. d
8. a

Vocabulary and Semantics 3
pp. 13-15
1. b
2. c
3. b
4. b
5. a
6. a
7. d

Vocabulary and Semantics 4
pp. 16-18
1. a
2. b
3. d
4. d
5. a
6. d
7. a
8. a

Vocabulary and Semantics 5
pp. 19-21
1. a
2. a
3. c
4. d
5. b
6. d
7. d

Vocabulary and Semantics 6
pp. 22-24
1. c
2. c
3. c
4. a
5. c
6. b
7. c
8. d

Vocabulary and Semantics 7
pp. 25-27
1. a
2. a
3. c
4. c
5. d
6. d
7. c

Vocabulary and Semantics 8
pp. 28-30
1. a
2. c
3. a
4. d
5. b
6. a
7. a
8. a

Vocabulary and Semantics 9
pp. 31-33
1. a
2. a
3. b
4. b
5. c
6. c
7. c

Vocabulary and Semantics 10
pp. 34-36
1. b
2. c
3. c
4. d
5. b
6. d
7. d

Sequencing 1
pp. 37-39
1. a
2. b
3. c
4. b
5. b
6. c
7. b
8. Before; she's on her way to school

Sequencing 2
pp. 40-42
1. b
2. b
3. a
4. b
5. a
6. b
7. a
8. Nighttime; Chad will go to bed after the show.

Answer Key, *continued*

Sequencing 3
pp. 43-45
1. a
2. c
3. b
4. c
5. b
6. a
7. c
8. Answers will vary.

Sequencing 4
pp. 46-48
1. a
2. c
3. a
4. c
5. b
6. c
7. a
8. Answers will vary.

Sequencing 5
pp. 49-51
1. b
2. c
3. b
4. a
5. c
6. a
7. b
8. Answers will vary.

Sequencing 6
pp. 52-54
1. a
2. b
3. a
4. a
5. b
6. a
7. c
8. Answers will vary.

Sequencing 7
pp. 55-57
1. b
2. a
3. c
4. b
5. b
6. a

7. c
8. Answers will vary.

Sequencing 8
pp. 58-60
1. b
2. b
3. a
4. a
5. a
6. c
7. b
8. Morning; they haven't had lunch yet.

Sequencing 9
pp. 61-63
1. b
2. b
3. a
4. b
5. c
6. b
7. b
8. Answers will vary.

Sequencing 10
pp. 64-66
1. a
2. b
3. a
4. b
5. a = 2
   b = 1
   c = 3
6. a
7. c
8. Answers will vary.

Comparing and Contrasting 1
pp. 67-69
1. b
2. a
3. a
4. b
5. a
6. b
7. a
8. b
9. b
10. a

Comparing and Contrasting 2
pp. 70-72
1. a
2. c
3. a
4. a
5. a
6. c
7. b
8. c

Comparing and Contrasting 3
pp. 73-75
1. a
2. d
3. d
4. b
5. c
6. b
7. c
8. c

Comparing and Contrasting 4
pp. 76-79
1. c
2. b
3. a
4. c
5. a
6. c
7. a
8. b
9. a
10. d
11. a
12. a

Comparing and Contrasting 5
pp. 80-82
1. c
2. a
3. d
4. b
5. a
6. c
7. a
8. c
9. c

Answer Key, *continued*

Comparing and Contrasting 6
pp. 83-85
1. b
2. d
3. b
4. a
5. c
6. a
7. a
8. a

Comparing and Contrasting 7
pp. 86-89
1. a
2. c
3. a
4. b
5. c
6. b
7. c
8. a
9. b
10. d

Comparing and Contrasting 8
pp. 90-92
1. a
2. d
3. b
4. a
5. c
6. a
7. a

Comparing and Contrasting 9
pp. 93-95
1. a
2. c
3. a
4. c
5. d
6. a
7. c
8. d

Comparing and Contrasting 10
pp. 96-98
1. a
2. c
3. d
4. d
5. c

6. b
7. a
8. c
9. b

Exclusion 1
pp. 99-101
1. c
2. a
3. c
4. a
5. c
6. a
7. a
8. c

Exclusion 2
pp. 102-104
1. b
2. b
3. b
4. c
5. c
6. a
7. c
8. a

Exclusion 3
pp. 105-107
1. a
2. b
3. b
4. c
5. a
6. c
7. c
8. a

Exclusion 4
pp. 108-110
1. b
2. a
3. b
4. a
5. c
6. a
7. a
8. b

Exclusion 5
pp. 111-113
1. c
2. b
3. c
4. a
5. b
6. c
7. a
8. Answers will vary.

Exclusion 6
pp. 114-116
1. a
2. d
3. b
4. b
5. b
6. b
7. c
8. c

Exclusion 7
pp. 117-119
1. c
2. c
3. a
4. a
5. c
6. b
7. b
8. b

Exclusion 8
pp. 120-122
1. a
2. d
3. b
4. a
5. d
6. b
7. c
8. Answers will vary.

Exclusion 9
pp. 123-125
1. c
2. b
3. c
4. b
5. b
6. a

Answer Key, *continued*

7. a
8. b

Exclusion 10
pp. 126-128
1. b
2. c
3. b
4. d
5. b
6. b
7. a
8. b

Problem Solving 1
pp. 129-131
1. b
2. c
3. a
4. b
5. a
6. c
7. b
8. c

Problem Solving 2
pp. 132-134
1. a
2. a
3. c
4. a
5. a
6. b
7. b
8. b

Problem Solving 3
pp. 135-137
1. a
2. a
3. b
4. b
5. b
6. c
7. b
8. a

Problem Solving 4
pp. 138-140
1. b
2. b
3. c

4. d
5. a
6. a
7. b
8. b

Problem Solving 5
pp. 141-143
1. a
2. c
3. a
4. b
5. c
6. a
7. a and c
8. b

Problem Solving 6
pp. 144-146
1. a
2. b
3. a
4. a
5. b
6. b
7. a
8. Answers will vary.

Problem Solving 7
pp. 147-149
1. a
2. c
3. c
4. c
5. a
6. b
7. a
8. a

Problem Solving 8
pp. 150-152
1. a
2. c
3. a
4. b
5. c
6. b
7. a
8. Answers will vary.

Problem Solving 9
pp. 153-155
1. a
2. a
3. c
4. c
5. b
6. b
7. d
8. Answers will vary.

Problem Solving 10
pp. 156-158
1. b
2. c
3. a
4. b
5. b
6. a
7. a
8. b

Characters and Actions 1
pp. 159-161
1. a
2. c
3. a
4. a
5. b
6. c
7. e
8. Answers will vary.

Characters and Actions 2
pp. 162-164
1. b
2. b
3. a
4. c
5. d
6. c
7. b
8. Answers will vary.

Characters and Actions 3
pp. 165-167
1. a
2. b
3. c
4. b
5. c
6. b

7. a
8. Answers will vary.

Characters and Actions 4
pp. 168-170
1. a
2. b
3. c
4. c
5. a
6. b
7. a
8. Answers will vary.

Characters and Actions 5
pp. 171-173
1. c
2. b
3. a
4. a
5. a
6. c
7. b
8. Answers will vary.

Characters and Actions 6
pp. 174-176
1. a
2. c
3. b
4. c
5. d
6. b
7. c
8. Answers will vary.

Characters and Actions 7
pp. 177-179
1. c
2. b
3. a
4. c
5. b
6. a
7. c
8. Answers will vary.

Characters and Actions 8
pp. 180-182
1. b
2. a
3. c

4. Answers will vary.
5. Answers will vary.
6. e
7. c
8. Answers will vary.

Characters and Actions 9
pp. 183-185
1. a
2. c
3. b
4. a
5. b
6. c
7. b
8. Answers will vary.

Characters and Actions 10
pp. 186-188
1. c
2. b
3. a
4. c
5. b
6. a
7. b
8. Answers will vary.

Figurative Language 1
pp. 189-191
1. b
2. a
3. c
4. True
5. b
6. False
7. b
8. c
9. b
10. a
11. Acting silly

Figurative Language 2
pp. 192-194
1. d
2. b
3. c
4. b
5. a
6. a
7. c
8. Very concerned

Figurative Language 3
pp. 195-197
1. a
2. c
3. b
4. b
5. a
6. a
7. d
8. b
9. I can't concentrate.

Figurative Language 4
pp. 198-200
1. b
2. b
3. a
4. c
5. a
6. b
7. c
8. Very old

Figurative Language 5
pp. 201-203
1. c
2. b
3. a
4. c
5. b
6. c
7. a
8. Weak and out of energy

Figurative Language 6
pp. 204-206
1. c
2. a
3. c
4. b
5. a
6. c
7. You look very nice.

Figurative Language 7
pp. 207-209
1. b
2. b
3. b
4. c
5. b
6. d

7. d
8. You can't tell what's going on if you just look on the surface.

Figurative Language 8
pp. 210-212
1. a
2. c
3. b
4. a
5. a
6. c
7. Don't spoil my happiness.

Figurative Language 9
pp. 213-215
1. c
2. a
3. b
4. a
5. d
6. Do it.

Figurative Language 10
pp. 216-218
1. a
2. c
3. b
4. a
5. c
6. c
7. d

Conclusions and Inferences 1
pp. 219-221
1. a
2. c
3. b
4. c
5. a
6. b
7. c

Conclusions and Inferences 2
pp. 222-224
1. b
2. d
3. a
4. b
5. c
6. b
7. a

Conclusions and Inferences 3
pp. 225-227
1. c
2. c
3. b
4. a
5. a
6. a

Conclusions and Inferences 4
pp. 228-230
1. d
2. c
3. b
4. a
5. c
6. b

Conclusions and Inferences 5
pp. 231-233
1. a
2. c
3. b
4. b
5. b
6. c
7. c
8. c

Conclusions and Inferences 6
pp. 234-236
1. c
2. a
3. a
4. b
5. a
6. c
7. b

Conclusions and Inferences 7
pp. 237-239
1. c
2. b
3. d
4. a
5. a
6. a
7. c

Conclusions and Inferences 8
pp. 240-242
1. b
2. c
3. b
4. a
5. c
6. a
7. b

Conclusions and Inferences 9
pp. 243-245
1. b
2. c
3. a
4. b
5. b
6. a
7. c
8. a

Conclusions and Inferences 10
pp. 246-248
1. b
2. a
3. b
4. b
5. c
6. a
7. c

Paraphrasing and Summarizing 1
pp. 249-251
1. b
2. a
3. c
4. b
5. a
6. b
7. c
8. Answers will vary.

Paraphrasing and Summarizing 2
pp. 252-254
1. b
2. b
3. c
4. b
5. a
6. b

Answer Key, *continued*

7. a. Spreads butter on bread
   b. Adds lettuce, tomato, cheese, and pickle slices
   c. Spreads mustard on bread and stacks it on top
8. Answers will vary.

Paraphrasing and Summarizing 3
pp. 255-257
1. b
2. c
3. a
4. c
5. b
6. b
7. b
8. Answers will vary.

Paraphrasing and Summarizing 4
pp. 258-260
1. b
2. c
3. c
4. c
5. a
6. b
7. b
8. Answers will vary.

Paraphrasing and Summarizing 5
pp. 261-263
1. c
2. a
3. c
4. a
5. c
6. b
7. a
8. Answers will vary.

Paraphrasing and Summarizing 6
pp. 264-266
1. a
2. a
3. c
4. a
5. c
6. b
7. c
8. Answers will vary.

Paraphrasing and Summarizing 7
pp. 267-269
1. c
2. b
3. b
4. c
5. a
6. c
7. a
8. Answers will vary.

Paraphrasing and Summarizing 8
pp. 270-272
1. c
2. b
3. c
4. b
5. a
6. c
7. a
8. Answers will vary.

Paraphrasing and Summarizing 9
pp. 273-275
1. c
2. b
3. c
4. b
5. c
6. a
7. b
8. Answers will vary.

Paraphrasing and Summarizing 10
pp. 276-278
1. a
2. c
3. c
4. b
5. b
6. c
7. b
8. Answers will vary.

14-03-987654321

Story Comprehension To Go   285   Copyright © 2003 LinguiSystems, Inc.